THE JAZZ AGE

THE AMERICAN CHARACTER SERIES

John C. Schweitzer, CONSULTING EDITOR

The Jazz Age

Edited by MAX BOGART

CHARLES SCRIBNER'S SONS

NEW YORK

ACKNOWLEDGMENTS

The editor is indebted to the following authors, publishers, and other holders of copyright for permission to use copyrighted materials.

Albert and Charles Boni, Inc., for "Taking the Cure, By the Shores of Cat Creek," by Will Rogers.

Brandt & Brandt for Chapter 8 of *Alice Adams*, by Booth

Tarkington, copyright 1921, Doubleday & Company, Inc.; copyright renewed 1948 by Susanah K. Tarkington. For "Invocation" from *John Brown's Body*, by Stephen Vincent Benét, Holt, Rinehart and Winston, Inc., copyright 1927, 1928 by Stephen Vincent Benét; copyright renewed 1955, 1956 by Rosemary Carr Benét.

Floyd Dell for "The Blanket," by Floyd Dell.

Doubleday & Company, Inc., for "certain maxims of archy," from *archy and mehitabel*, by Don Marquis, copyright 1927 by Doubleday & Company.

Norma Millay Ellis, Literary Executor, for "Lament," "First Fig," "Second Fig," "Justice Denied in Massachusetts," and "Recuerdo," from *Collected Poems of Edna St. Vincent Millay*, Harper & Row, copyright 1921, 1928, 1948, 1950, 1955 by Edna St. Vincent Millay and Norma Millay Ellis.

Harcourt, Brace & World, Inc., for Chapter 1 from *Babbitt*, by Sinclair Lewis, copyright 1922 by Harcourt, Brace & World, Inc.; renewed 1950 by Sinclair Lewis. For "Jazz Fantasia" and "Four Preludes on Playthings of the Winds," from *Smoke and Steel*, by Carl Sandburg, copyright 1920 by Harcourt, Brace & World, Inc.; renewed 1948 by Carl Sandburg.

Harper & Row, Publishers, Incorporated, for "Yet Do I Marvel" and "Incident," copyright 1925 by Harper & Brothers; renewed 1953 by Ida M. Cullen; and for "From the Dark Tower," copyright 1927 by Harper & Brothers; renewed 1955 by Ida M. Cullen—all from *On These I Stand* (1947), by Countee Cullen.

Holt, Rinehart and Winston, Inc., for "Prayers of Steel" and "Grass," from *Cornhuskers*, by Carl Sandburg, copyright 1918 by Holt, Rinehart and Winston, Inc., copyright 1946 by Carl Sandburg. For "The Onset," "Stopping by Woods on a Snowy Evening," "Fire and Ice," "Acceptance," and "Acquainted with the Night," from *Complete Poems of Robert Frost*, copyright 1923, 1928, 1934 by Holt, Rinehart and Winston, Inc.; copyright 1951, © 1956, 1962 by Robert Frost.

Alfred A. Knopf, Inc., for "Paul's Case," reprinted from *Youth and the Bright Medusa*, by Willa Cather. For "The Weary Blues," "Cross," and "I Too Sing America," copyright 1926 by Alfred A. Knopf, Inc., and renewed 1954 by Langston Hughes; reprinted from *Selected Poems of Langston Hughes*. For "Lenox Avenue, Midnight," copyright 1926 by Alfred A. Knopf, Inc., and renewed 1954 by Langston Hughes, reprinted from *The Weary Blues*, by Langston Hughes. For "The Libido for the Ugly," copyright 1927 by Alfred A. Knopf, Inc., and renewed 1955 by H. L. Mencken, reprinted from *A Mencken Chrestomathy*, by H. L. Mencken.

The Macmillan Company for "The Dark Hills" and "Mr. Flood's Party," copyright 1920 and 1921 by Edwin Arlington Robinson; renewed 1942 and 1949 by Ruth Nivison; and for "Why He Was There," "Glass Houses," and "The Garden of Nations," copyright 1925 by The Macmillan Company; renewed 1952 by Ruth Nivison and Barbara R. Holt—all from *Collected Poems of Edwin Arlington Robinson*. For "A Net to Snare the Moonlight," copyright 1913 by The Macmillan Company; and for "The Scientific Aspiration" and "Another Word on the Scientific Aspiration," copyright 1920 by The Macmillan Company; renewed 1948 by Elizabeth C. Lindsay—all from *Collected Poems of Vachel Lindsay*.

Ellen C. Masters for "Jacob Mordant," "Merritt Larkin," and "Mary Nolen," from *The New Spoon River*, by Edgar Lee Masters, The Macmillan Company.

Charles Scribner's Sons for "Soldier's Home," from *In Our Time*, by Ernest Hemingway, copyright 1925 by Charles Scribner's Sons; renewal copyright 1953 Ernest Hemingway. For "Winter Dreams," copyright 1922 Frances Scott Fitzgerald Lanahan; renewal copyright 1950; reprinted from *All the Sad Young Men*, by F. Scott Fitzgerald. For selection from Chapter 37, pages 483–487, of *Look Homeward Angel*, by Thomas Wolfe, copyright 1929 Charles Scribner's Sons; renewal copyright © 1957 Edward C. Aswell and Fred W. Wolfe. For "Haircut," copyright 1925 by Ellis A. Lardner; renewal copyright 1953; reprinted from *The Love Nest and Other Stories*, by Ring Lardner.

Twayne Publishers, Inc., for "America," by Claude McKay.

The Viking Press, Inc., for "The Waltz," by Dorothy Parker, from *The Portable Dorothy Parker*, copyright 1933 © 1961 by Dorothy Parker; originally appeared in *The New Yorker*. For "One Perfect Rose" from *The Portable Dorothy Parker*, copyright 1926, 1954 by Dorothy Parker. For "Hands" from *Winesburg, Ohio*, by Sherwood Anderson, copyright 1919 by B. W. Huebsch, Inc.; 1947 by Eleanor Copenhaver Anderson. For "The Creation," from *God's Trombones*, by James Weldon Johnson, copyright 1927 by the Viking Press, Inc.; 1955 by Grace Nail Johnson.

The World Publishing Company, for "The Second Choice," from *Free and Other Stories*, by Theodore Dreiser, copyright © 1918 by Boni & Liveright; copyright © 1945 by Theodore Dreiser.

CONTENTS

CRITICISM AND COMMENTARY

DRAMA IN THE JAZZ AGE

THE JAZZ AGE

Here was a new generation . . . grown up to find all
Gods dead, all wars fought, all faiths in man shaken.

—F. SCOTT FITZGERALD, *This Side of Paradise*

INTRODUCTION

The decade following World War I has been labeled
"the roaring twenties," "the fabulous twenties" and "the
Jazz Age." It was a peculiar historical period, perhaps more
schizophrenic than any era before or since, for it was marked
by sharp contrasts: certainty and insecurity, stability and confusion, content and discontent, and conformity and rebellion
in a time of peace and prosperity. It was an age dominated by
science, technology and the new machines, yet it was a time
that produced significant contributions in literature and other
art forms. It was reminiscent of certain ages and societies
which, at the height of their power and wealth, were followed
by abrupt declines and dark days. Although comparisons may
be suggested, the Jazz Age represents an era and a state of
mind that remains unique in the history of the United States.

In the 1920's America was in the midst of a period of
prosperity never before known in the world. Economists have
pointed out that it required only a small amount of money to
be considered "well-off" in the twenties because the level of
prices and taxes was low. It is estimated that a person earning

$6,000 or more a year was in a select income group, approximately the upper five percent of the population. In reality, this was a brief boom, a precarious period of prosperity lasting for a scant five years. Business thrived; earnings and profits rose to new heights. Big business, the economists asserted, was responsible for the prosperity, and throughout the period, the giant industries, with a minimum of government restraint, merged into ever-larger corporations.

The domestic social reforms and social legislation initiated by President Theodore Roosevelt and carried on by President Woodrow Wilson in the pre-World War I years were abandoned in the twenties. Politically, the period was marked by conservatism, inertia, apathy and indifference. In an overwhelming victory in 1920 the Republicans elected Warren G. Harding, who died in 1923; Calvin Coolidge succeeded him and then served a full term beginning in 1924. Herbert Hoover was elected President in 1928. The three presidents held the confidence of the business sector; all won by large majorities; all represented the standpat views of "normalcy" in a Republican era. A wave of popular reaction set in against public planning, economic control and social responsibility. Most Americans paid little attention to inadequate housing, unemployment (existing even during the prosperity years), run-down factory towns and abandoned mine communities, and the plight of the farmer. Major strikes were not uncommon in the post-World War I period; the most sensational were those of the steelworkers, the coal miners and the Boston police.

The short-lived period of prosperity was the beginning of the age of accelerated mass production. New inventions and the improvement of assembly line techniques produced more goods at prices within the reach of people who previously could not afford them. The rise of chain stores and an increased number of department stores with new methods of quantity buying, distributing and merchandising made more products available to millions of consumers.

With the ever-increasing production of automobiles the 1920's saw man conquering distance in a way that hardly seemed possible a few years before. The average family now owned an automobile; there were over 23 million on the road in 1929, and the tempo of life was speeded up. Twelve million families owned radios, recently invented. Women although they won political equality, voting for the first time in 1920 as a result of the Nineteenth Amendment, gained their real freedom with the availability of new household appliances, such as vacuum cleaners and washing machines.

With the increased use of the airplane, especially following Charles A. Lindbergh's dramatic trans-Atlantic solo flight in 1927, the general population became familiar with air power and the possibilities of its ultimate conquest of space. This was, indeed, the age of the machine with its power to affect the human being's senses. Silent motion pictures provided mankind with a lens on the world; the "talking" movies and radio opened the audio domain. In 1920 regular commercial broadcasting was initiated. The machine's future possibilities were unlimited and promised mankind more free time, more necessities at lower prices, more comforts hitherto unobtainable and a better way of life for all. Merle Curti wrote in *The Growth of American Thought:* "No wonder that the machine became celebrated as the eighth wonder of the world, destined to set man free."

But several writers raised serious questions about the machine's providing a Utopia for mankind. Irwin Edman warned that the machine would promote the standardization of life; Sherwood Anderson asserted it would destroy man's creative work; and Stuart Chase and Lewis Mumford argued that unless the machine was subordinated to the will of man, it would ultimately destroy society.

Nonetheless, the machine age brought higher wages and a shortened working week, providing undreamed of leisure time to participate in recreational activities. Attendance at sporting events set new records. This was the golden age of sports, with glittering performances by Babe Ruth in baseball, Jack Dempsey in boxing, Red Grange in football, Bobby Jones in golf, Bill Tilden in tennis and Gertrude Ederle in swimming the English Channel. It was also the era that saw the beginning of bathing beauty contests, a craze for crossword puzzles, marathon dancing and flagpole sitting. It was an age of hero worship. Millions of women adored Rudolph Valentino, a star of the silent screen, and millions acclaimed Charles A. Lindbergh.

As people reflected on World War I ("the war to end war," the war "to make the world safe for democracy,") many concluded the conflict was a national mistake. From their disillusionment came a feeling of bitterness, hostility toward international affairs, and an intensification of nationalistic feelings.

America assumed an isolationist position, avoiding international involvement except for conferences on disarmament. The press attacked internationalism in all forms. Despite President Wilson's pleas, the dream of a world body of government, the League of Nations, was abandoned by Congress. As the American people assessed the chaotic conditions in Europe, which in the twenties was struggling to reform its economic and social systems, many concluded that the United States should remain aloof from the decadent mess in the Old World.

The growth of nationalism, together with the reaction against internationalism, resulted in an American attitude of superiority toward the rest of the world. Newspapers and magazines focused on the superiority theme, asserting that the United States was the "only first-class civilization in the world today." Certain publications announced America's superiority was derived from the "Nordic" strains and "Nordic race." Little wonder that Carl Sandburg bitterly cried out, "Nothing like us ever was."

Post-World War I was a time of superpatriotism; certain government agencies and private groups were involved in extremist actions. Probably the most flagrant violations of constitutional rights came as a result of the "red scare" raids against political radicals by Attorney General Mitchell Palmer. In one day, January 1, 1920, he jailed some 6,000 suspects, and his crusade led to the deportation of aliens suspected of un-American activities.

Many people believe that the Sacco-Vanzetti case, the *cause célèbre* of the 1920's, resulted from the atmosphere of suspicion. In 1920 Nicola Sacco, a shoe-factory worker, and Bartolomeo Vanzetti, a fish peddler, were arrested and charged with a payroll robbery and murder in South Braintree, Massachusetts. Both men were immigrants, radicals, pacifists and anarchists; they were known as leftist agitators engaged in the labor struggle. Everywhere people debated the guilt or innocence of the two men and the country was divided in judging the case. Although supported by many prominent persons from the professions, Sacco and Vanzetti were found guilty and executed in 1927. To this day many think that they were convicted on questionable evidence and because of hostility toward their political beliefs.

The Jazz Age is also remembered for violent acts of intolerance and bigotry, the backlash directed not only at political radicals, labor leaders and unions, and aliens, but also at Catholics, Jews and Negroes. Severe race riots erupted in twenty-six cities and towns, including Chicago, East St. Louis and Washington, D.C.

Nationalism in its most vicious and violent form was masked in white bed sheets. The Ku Klux Klan, originally formed during the Reconstruction Period after the Civil War, revived in the 1920's and terrorized many communities in several Southern and Midwestern states. With the slogan "native, white, Protestant supremacy," relying on fear, ignorance and superstition, responsible for countless beatings, floggings and murders, the Klan grew to about five million members by 1925, according to estimates at the time.

Religious fundamentalism was supported in the laws of certain Southern states; these laws proclaimed against the teaching of the theory of evolution. The now famous Scopes trial in Dayton, Tennessee, became the test case of the fundamentalist attitude. John T. Scopes, a teacher of science, was charged with violating the state law forbidding the teaching of evolution. Clarence Darrow, recognized as the greatest trial lawyer of the period, defended Scopes. Prosecuting in the name of the law and voicing the fundamentalist view was William Jennings Bryan, renowned orator and Democratic nominee for the Presidency in three campaigns. Although Darrow triumphed in the savage debate with Bryan, Scopes was found guilty and fined three hundred dollars. The trial, fully covered by the press, including H. L. Mencken, focused sharply on ignorance and shocked millions of Americans.

A new morality emerged in the twenties. On campuses throughout the country young people ("flaming youth") were in revolt against Victorian standards of manners and morals, and against the Puritan reticence concerning sex.

Historians, sociologists and psychologists provide many answers for the breakdown of the old order—the growth of many large cities, the war and its economic restraints, the general collapse of idealism, and the conviction that the war was a mistake.

Certain analysts found the Volstead Act, known as "Prohibition," mainly responsible for the decay of law and morality and for the beginning of a crime explosion. In any event, once the law became effective on January 16, 1920, countless violations occurred throughout the country during the twenties because enforcing prohibition was an impossible task. Alcoholic beverages were illegally manufactured; gangster organizations grew, gaining enormous profits and control not only of the illicit alcohol market but also of gambling, prostitution and narcotics. Smuggling alcohol across the Canadian and Mexican borders and by ships ("rum runners") along both ocean coastlines was a daily occurrence; illegal sales ("bootlegging") seemingly took place everywhere in the modern saloons: the roadhouses and the "speakeasies." These gangster-operated "rackets" flourished. Ironically, in the prohibition era drinking by young people increased immeasurably.

Some critics cite loose interpretation of Dr. Sigmund Freud's writings as a major factor in the sex revolution of the twenties. Many falsely concluded that serious maladjustment resulted from suppression of sexual desire and that free sexual expression was normal behavior.

The decline of strict moral standards resulted in a permissive atmosphere of wild parties, open discussion of sex, short skirts, women's use of lipstick and cosmetics, "petting" or "necking," college campus drinking, the rise of tabloids emphasizing scandal, sex and violence, the increased number of "confession" magazines, and movies with frank sex scenes, previously censored. The automobile, now readily available for young people, provided opportunities for "petting" away from home, a behavior pattern unknown previously.

During this period "silent" motion pictures came of age; serious films were produced featuring significant and provocative topics. Leading figures of the silent screen were the comedians Charlie Chaplin and Harold Lloyd; "America's sweetheart," Mary Pickford; swashbuckling Douglas Fairbanks; Rudolph Valentino, known as "the great lover"; and director Cecil B. de Mille, whose films included casts of thousands and spectacular scenery. Many films, reflecting the morals revolution, exploited sexual themes and starred sex-symbol heroines.

At the end of the decade about 23,000 motion picture theatres attracted an estimated 100 million weekly admissions. In addition to their popular entertainment appeal, movies exerted a tremendous influence in shaping the values and attitudes of the American people. Their appeal and influence increased after the production of the first "all-talking" film in 1927 (*The Jazz Singer* with Al Jolson) and the perfection of sound techniques in later films.

The prosperity of the twenties hastened the expansion and improvement of public schools, resulting in a sharp decline of illiteracy. Secondary education became almost universal with 4 million students in 1925 as compared to 1.5 million ten years before. Colleges expanded, too, with 867,000 in 1928 compared to 462,000 at the beginning of the decade.

All religious denominations increased their memberships, but the United States remained a predominantly Protestant nation in the 1920's.

Newspaper circulation continued to rise sharply, especially because of the growth of newspaper chains such as Hearst and Scripps-Howard. Standardized news services, the Associated Press and United Press, and features (columns, comics, or "funnies," and cartoons), increased not only in the chain operations but also in the independent newspapers. Gradually, the press became ever more dependent on advertising for revenues. The post-World War I era saw the appearance of tabloids in many large cities; these newspapers were distinguished by a minimum of news material, an abundance of photographs, sensational reports on violence, and more features than in conventional dailies.

Among the most widely read weekly and monthly magazines were *The Saturday Evening Post, Collier's, Liberty,* and the "women's magazines" (*Ladies Home Journal, Woman's Home Companion, Cosmopolitan* and *Redbook,* for example). Four of today's major periodicals first appeared in the twenties: *The Reader's Digest* (1922), *The Saturday Review of Literature* (1924), *Time* (1925), and *The New Yorker* (1925). *Harper's, Scribner's* and *The Atlantic Monthly* were magazines widely read by serious readers, but *The Nation, The New Republic, The American Mercury* and *The Smart Set* voiced the views of many American intellectuals.

In the midst of surface gaiety a small but influential group of writers expressed their disappointment and disillusionment. "We are a lost generation," wrote Gertrude Stein; and F. Scott Fitzgerald described American society as "the beautiful and the damned." The social critics stated their frustrations and despair, and critical ferment pervaded the 1920's.

The intellectuals, described by *The American Mercury* as the "civilized minority," attacked the hypocrisy, conformity, standardization and fraudulent aspects of American life.

They criticized the mediocrity and anti-intellectualism of the people, their taste in popular music, magazines and "yellow" journals. Philosophers deplored the debasing of standards and breakdown of morals. Social critics constantly pointed out that America's quest for culture was superficial and, therefore, doomed.

The major literary rebel of the twenties was H. L. Mencken. Describing the people as "booboisie," "homo boobiens" and "boobus Americanus," Mencken ridiculed democracy, "organized" religion, prohibition, hero worship, business and businessmen, Philistinism, prominent public figures, censorship, morality, education and professors, fraternal orders, reformers, patriotism and quackery of all kinds. By the end of the decade he was widely read and unusually influential.

T. S. Eliot, Ezra Pound and other American writers rebelled by self-exile to Europe. Many, however, remained, expressing their views about America in their literary works.

Sinclair Lewis, the most widely read novelist of the twenties, satirically exposed the drabness and ugliness of life in the Midwestern small town, the sterility of American culture, the petty prejudices of little people, the smugness of middle-class businessmen, and the hypocritical values of the times. His chief works in the decade were *Main Street* (1920), *Babbitt* (1922), *Arrowsmith* (1925), *Elmer Gantry* (1927) and *Dodsworth* (1929).

Certain literary critics and historians think that Theodore Dreiser dominated the era with his *An American Tragedy* (1925), a novel symbolic of the times. Certainly Dreiser, dealing with environmental factors, was a leading figure in the naturalistic revolt against the romantic tradition in American literature. Other major naturalists were Sherwood Anderson,

John Dos Passos and Ernest Hemingway. Anderson's psychological probing into the minds of small-town people in *Winesburg, Ohio* (1919) and in other works of fiction questioned the meaning of life and exposed the hypocrisies in small-town America. In *Three Soldiers* (1921) Dos Passos described the demoralization and degradation of men in uniform at the end of World War I. In *A Farewell to Arms* (1929) Hemingway expressed the disillusionment of the "lost generation" and indicted the sham ideals as he had previously in *The Sun Also Rises* (1926) and *Men and Women* (1927).

F. Scott Fitzgerald's fiction, though, became the symbol of the 1920's. No other writer captured so well the spirit of the Jazz Age, the moral decay of his generation, and it is doubtful whether any other literary artist appealed to youth as much as Fitzgerald. In *This Side of Paradise* (1920), *The Beautiful and Damned* (1922) and especially in *The Great Gatsby* (1925), he seemed to speak for his generation's despair and alienation.

Several important writers of the twenties were not involved in the naturalistic revolt but nevertheless produced a body of quality literature. Among this group were Edith Wharton, Ellen Glasgow, Willa Cather and Dorothy Canfield Fisher. Thomas Wolfe also showed great promise in his romantic revolt against his home town and a domineering, materialistic mother in *Look Homeward, Angel* (1929).

Poetry of the 1920's ranges from the realistic to the romantic, from harsh and bitter views to serene and lofty statements, and from experimental forms in free verse to traditional modes. Several poets produced major works during the decade. Robert Frost expressed his love of nature, and his views on the dignity of the individual and the simple life. Carl Sandburg wrote sympathetic pieces about the common man. Edwin Arlington Robinson stated his hatred of materialism in eloquent music and imagery. Edna St. Vincent Millay voiced her feelings in romantic, lyrical forms. Robinson Jeffers savagely assaulted humanity in his major poems; Archibald MacLeish recorded his discontent with the times; E. E. Cummings created a highly experimental style; and Stephen Vincent Benét's major contribution was a widely read epic poem on the Civil War.

Although American writers created significant fiction and poetry during the Jazz Age, the drama, except for Eugene O'Neill, was not an important *genre*. Major plays of O'Neill were *The Long Voyage Home* (1919), *The Emperor Jones* (1920), *The Hairy Ape* (1922), *Desire Under the Elms* (1924), and *Strange Interlude* (1928). Dealing for the most part with realistic, Freudian themes, O'Neill's work was markedly different from the uncomplicated realism of other plays of the time: *What Price Glory* (1924) by Maxwell Anderson and Laurence Stallings, *They Knew What They Wanted* (1924) by Sidney Howard, and *Street Scene* (1929) by Elmer Rice.

Jazz was the major contribution of music to the twenties. Ragtime evolved into jazz with composers such as George Gershwin and Cole Porter producing many catchy, popular tunes. Near the end of the decade Gershwin composed two significant works, which, according to the critics, made jazz a respectable art form: *Rhapsody in Blue* (1927) and *An American in Paris* (1928). Musical plays were much in evidence with such "hits" as *Show Boat*, based on a novel by Edna Ferber, transformed for the theatre by Jerome Kern and Oscar Hammerstein II. The romantic operettas of Sigmund Romberg, *The Student Prince* and *Desert Song*, played to capacity audiences in the 1920's. One of the most popular songs of the decade was "Yes, We Have No Bananas."

During the twenties Americans showed a growing interest in the visual arts. Generally, the art was influenced by the European schools of abstract and primitive painting, cubism, and surrealism. Among the leading American abstract painters were John Marin, Charles R. Sheeler and Max Weber. Certain artists, however, adhered to the graphic realism tradition of painting in the pre-World War I period; among these were George Bellows, Edward Hopper and John Sloan. In architecture the influence of Louis Sullivan and Frank Lloyd Wright, the concept that form follows function, was evident in a number of new structures.

The Jazz Age came to an abrupt end in 1929. Over a million Americans were investors in the stock market; many were speculators seeking fast, high profits. While some speculators were successful, others overextended themselves by buying with borrowed capital. The economic boom of the twenties evolved into economic panic in October 1929. On October 24 the market broke as stocks plummeted. Many stocks became worthless, and by October 29 the collapse was clearly evident. The market's decline marked the end of the Jazz Age and the beginning of the Great Depression. As Frederick Lewis Allen points out in *Only Yesterday*, this not only meant an economic crash but its implications for Americans in the years that followed were incalculable. Allen notes that as the era of prosperity was dying, Americans faced a new kind of life which required ". . . new adjustments, new ideas, new habits of thought, and a new order of values."

A few months later, Marc Connelly, speaking through the Angel Gabriel in his play, *The Green Pastures*, aptly described the new era in these words: "Everything nailed down is comin' loose."

To understand the times and to comprehend the

nature of the American character, an exploration of representative works of literature should be helpful. Certain literary insights and outlooks reveal much about the American people and the tone of the twenties.

Max Bogart

FICTION

Willa Cather (1876–1947)

Novelist and short-story writer, Willa Cather achieved a reputation as a superior craftsman, disciplined with the ability to use the right word in the right place, and noted for her clarity of expression. Her character studies, using simple, traditional forms of fiction, reveal a sincerity and a profound sympathy for the people of the prairies, whose experiences of pioneer life she presents in several novels. Miss Cather's warmth of feeling and her sensitivity to the plight of young people are shown in "Paul's Case."

Born in Winchester, Virginia, Willa Cather spent her formative years in Nebraska. She was graduated from the University of Nebraska, taught English in the public schools of Pittsburgh, Pennsylvania, and later became editor of McClure's Magazine in New York City. In 1923 Miss Cather was awarded a Pulitzer Prize for her novel One of Ours.

PAUL'S CASE

It was Paul's afternoon to appear before the faculty of the Pittsburgh High School to account for his various misdemeanors. He had been suspended a week ago, and his father had called at the Principal's office and confessed his perplexity about his son. Paul entered the faculty room suave and smiling. His clothes were a trifle outgrown, and the tan velvet on the collar of his open overcoat was frayed and worn; but for all that there was something of the dandy about him, and he wore an opal pin in his neatly knotted black four-in-hand, and a red carnation in his buttonhole. This latter adornment the faculty somehow felt was not properly significant of the contrite spirit befitting a boy under the ban of suspension.

Paul was tall for his age and very thin, with high, cramped shoulders and a narrow chest. His eyes were remarkable for a certain hysterical brilliancy, and he continually used them in a conscious, theatrical sort of way, peculiarly offensive in a boy. The pupils were abnormally large, as though he were addicted to belladonna, but there was a glassy glitter about them which that drug does not produce.

When questioned by the Principal as to why he was there, Paul stated, politely enough, that he wanted to come back to school. This was a lie, but Paul was quite accustomed to lying; found it, indeed, indispensable for overcoming friction. His teachers were asked to state their respective charges against him, which they did with such a rancor and aggrievedness as evinced that this was not a usual case. Disorder and impertinence were among the offences named, yet each of his instructors felt that it was scarcely possible to put into words the real cause of the trouble, which lay in a sort of hysterically defiant manner of the boy's; in the contempt which they all knew he felt for them, and which he seemingly made not the least effort to conceal. Once, when he had been making a synopsis of a paragraph at the blackboard, his English teacher had stepped to his side and attempted to guide his hand. Paul had started back with a shudder and thrust his hands violently behind him. The astonished woman could scarcely have been more hurt and embarrassed had he struck at her. The insult was so involuntary and definitely personal as to be unforgettable. In one way and another, he had made all his teachers, men and women alike, conscious of the same feeling of physical aversion. In one class he habitually sat with his hand shading his eyes; in another he always looked out of the window during the recitation; in another he made a running commentary on the lecture with humorous intent.

His teachers felt this afternoon that his whole attitude was symbolized by his shrug and his flippantly red carnation flower, and they fell upon him without mercy, his English teacher leading the pack. He stood through it smiling, his pale lips parted over his white teeth. (His lips were continually twitching, and he had a habit of raising his eyebrows that was contemptuous and irritating to the last degree.) Older boys than Paul had broken down and shed tears under that ordeal, but his set smile did not once desert him, and his only sign of discomfort was the nervous trembling of the fingers that toyed with the buttons of his overcoat, and an occasional jerking of the other hand which held his hat. Paul was always smiling, always glancing about him, seeming to feel that people might be watching him and trying to detect something. This conscious expression, since it was as far as possible from boyish mirthfulness, was usually attributed to insolence or "smartness."

As the inquisition proceeded, one of his instructors repeated an impertinent remark of the boy's, and the Principal asked him whether he thought that a courteous speech to make to a woman. Paul shrugged his shoulders slightly and his eyebrows twitched.

"I don't know," he replied. "I didn't mean to be polite

or impolite, either. I guess it's a sort of way I have of saying things regardless."

The Principal asked him whether he didn't think that a way it would be well to get rid of. Paul grinned and said he guessed so. When he was told that he could go, he bowed gracefully and went out. His bow was like a repetition of the scandalous red carnation.

His teachers were in despair, and his drawing master voiced the feeling of them all when he declared there was something about the boy which none of them understood. He added: "I don't really believe that smile of his comes altogether from insolence; there's something sort of haunted about it. The boy is not strong, for one thing. There is something wrong about the fellow."

The drawing master had come to realize that, in looking at Paul, one saw only his white teeth and the forced animation of his eyes. One warm afternoon the boy had gone to sleep at his drawing-board, and his master had noted with amazement what a white, blue-veined face it was; drawn and wrinkled like an old man's about the eyes, the lips twitching even in his sleep.

His teachers left the building dissatisfied and unhappy; humiliated to have felt so vindictive toward a mere boy, to have uttered this feeling in cutting terms, and to have set each other on, as it were, in the gruesome game of intemperate reproach. One of them remembered having seen a miserable street cat set at bay by a ring of tormentors.

As for Paul, he ran down the hill whistling the Soldiers' Chorus from *Faust*, looking wildly behind him now and then to see whether some of his teachers were not there to witness his light-heartedness. As it was now late in the afternoon and Paul was on duty that evening as usher at

Carnegie Hall, he decided that he would not go home to supper.

When he reached the concert hall the doors were not yet open. It was chilly outside, and he decided to go up into the picture gallery—always deserted at this hour—where there were some of Raffelli's gay studies of Paris streets and an airy blue Venetian scene or two that always exhilarated him. He was delighted to find no one in the gallery but the old guard, who sat in the corner, a newspaper on his knee, a black patch over one eye and the other closed. Paul possessed himself of the place and walked confidently up and down, whistling under his breath. After a while he sat down before a blue Rico and lost himself. When he bethought him to look at his watch, it was after seven o'clock, and he rose with a start and ran downstairs, making a face at Augustus Cæsar, peering out from the cast room, and an evil gesture at the Venus of Milo as he passed her on the stairway.

When Paul reached the ushers' dressing room half a dozen boys were there already, and he began excitedly to tumble into his uniform. It was one of the few that at all approached fitting, and Paul thought it very becoming— though he knew the tight, straight coat accentuated his narrow chest, about which he was exceedingly sensitive. He was always excited when he dressed, twanging all over to the tuning of the strings and the preliminary flourishes of the horns in the music room; but tonight he seemed quite beside himself, and he teased and plagued the boys until, telling him that he was crazy, they put him down on the floor and sat on him.

Somewhat calmed by his suppression, Paul dashed out to the front of the house to seat the early comers. He was a model usher. Gracious and smiling he ran up and down the aisles. Nothing was too much trouble for him; he carried messages and brought programs as though it were his greatest pleasure in life, and all the people in his section thought him a charming boy, feeling that he remembered and admired them. As the house filled, he grew more and more vivacious and animated, and the color came to his cheeks and lips. It was very much as though this were a great reception and Paul were the host. Just as the musicians came to take their places, his English teacher arrived with checks for the seats which a prominent manufacturer had taken for the season. She betrayed some embarrassment when she handed Paul the tickets, and a *hauteur* which subsequently made her feel very foolish. Paul was startled for a moment, and had the feeling of wanting to put her out; what business had she here among all these fine people and gay colors? He looked her over and decided that she was not appropriately dressed and must be a fool to sit downstairs in such togs. The tickets had probably been sent her out of kindness, he reflected, as he put down a seat for her, and she had about as much right to sit there as he had.

When the symphony began Paul sank into one of the rear seats with a long sigh of relief, and lost himself as he had done before the Rico. It was not that symphonies, as such, meant anything in particular to Paul, but the first sigh of the instruments seemed to free some hilarious spirit within him; something that struggled there like the Genius in the bottle found by the Arab fisherman. He felt a sudden zest of life; the lights danced before his eyes and the concert hall blazed into unimaginable splendor. When the soprano soloist came on, Paul forgot even the nastiness of his teacher's being there, and gave himself up to the peculiar intoxication such personages always had for him. The soloist chanced to be a

German woman, by no means in her first youth, and the mother of many children; but she wore a satin gown and a tiara, and she had that indefinable air of achievement, that world-shine upon her, which always blinded Paul to any possible defects.

After a concert was over, Paul was often irritable and wretched until he got to sleep—and tonight he was even more than usually restless. He had the feeling of not being able to let down; of its being impossible to give up this delicious excitement which was the only thing that could be called living at all. During the last number he withdrew and, after hastily changing his clothes in the dressing room, slipped out to the side door where the singer's carriage stood. Here he began pacing rapidly up and down the walk, waiting to see her come out.

Over yonder the Schenley, in its vacant stretch, loomed big and square through the fine rain, the windows of its twelve stories glowing like those of a lighted cardboard house under a Christmas tree. All the actors and singers of any importance stayed there when they were in the city, and a number of the big manufacturers of the place lived there in the winter. Paul had often hung about the hotel, watching the people go in and out, longing to enter and leave schoolmasters and dull care behind him forever.

At last the singer came out, accompanied by the conductor, who helped her into her carriage and closed the door with a cordial *auf wiedersehen*—which set Paul to wondering whether she were not an old sweetheart of his. Paul followed the carriage over to the hotel, walking so rapidly as not to be far from the entrance when the singer alighted and disappeared behind the swinging glass doors which were opened by a Negro in a tall hat and a long coat. In the moment that the door was ajar, it seemed to Paul that he, too, entered. He seemed to feel himself go after her up the steps, into the warm, lighted building, into an exotic, a tropical world of shiny, glistening surfaces and basking ease. He reflected upon the mysterious dishes that were brought into the dining room, the green bottles in buckets of ice, as he had seen them in the supper party pictures of the Sunday supplement. A quick gust of wind brought the rain down with sudden vehemence, and Paul was startled to find that he was still outside in the slush of the gravel driveway; that his boots were letting in the water and his scanty overcoat was clinging wet about him; that the lights in front of the concert hall were out, and that the rain was driving in sheets between him and the orange glow of the windows above him. There it was, what he wanted—tangibly before him like the fairy world of a Christmas pantomime; as the rain beat in his face, Paul wondered whether he were destined always to shiver in the black night outside, looking up at it.

He turned and walked reluctantly toward the car tracks. The end had to come some time; his father in his night clothes at the top of the stairs, explanations that did not explain, hastily improvised fictions that were forever tripping him up, his upstairs room and its horrible yellow wallpaper, the creaking bureau with the greasy plush collar box, and over his painted wooden bed the pictures of George Washington and John Calvin, and the framed motto, "Feed my Lambs," which had been worked in red worsted by his mother, whom Paul could not remember.

Half an hour later Paul alighted from the Negley Avenue car and went slowly down one of the side streets off the main thoroughfare. It was a highly respectable street, where all the houses were exactly alike, and where business-

men of moderate means begot and reared large families of
children, all of whom went to Sabbath school and learned the
shorter catechism, and were interested in arithmetic; all of
whom were as exactly alike as their homes, and of a piece
with the monotony in which they lived. Paul never went up
Cordelia Street without a shudder of loathing. His home was
next the house of the Cumberland minister. He approached
it tonight with the nerveless sense of defeat, the hopeless
feeling of sinking back forever into ugliness and commonness
that he had always had when he came home. The moment he
turned into Cordelia Street he felt the waters close above his
head. After each of these orgies of living, he experienced all
the physical depression which follows a debauch; the loathing
of respectable beds, of common food, of a house permeated
by kitchen odours; a shuddering repulsion for the flavourless,
colourless mass of everyday existence; a morbid desire for
cool things and soft lights and fresh flowers.

The nearer he approached the house, the more absolutely unequal Paul felt to the sight of it all; his ugly sleeping
chamber; the cold bathroom with the grimy zinc tub, the
cracked mirror, the dripping spigots; his father, at the top of
the stairs, his hairy legs sticking out from his nightshirt, his
feet thrust into carpet slippers. He was so much later than
usual that there would certainly be inquiries and reproaches.
Paul stopped short before the door. He felt that he could not
be accosted by his father tonight; that he could not toss
again on that miserable bed. He would not go in. He would
tell his father that he had no carfare, and it was raining so
hard he had gone home with one of the boys and stayed all
night.

Meanwhile, he was wet and cold. He went around to
the back of the house and tried one of the basement win-

dows, found it open, raised it cautiously, and scrambled down
the cellar wall to the floor. There he stood, holding his
breath, terrified by the noise he had made; but the floor above
him was silent, and there was no creak on the stairs. He
found a soap-box, and carried it over to the soft ring of light
that streamed from the furnace door, and sat down. He was
horribly afraid of rats, so he did not try to sleep, but sat
looking distrustfully at the dark, still terrified lest he might
have awakened his father. In such reactions, after one of the
experiences which made days and nights out of the dreary
blanks of the calendar, when his senses were deadened, Paul's
head was always singularly clear. Suppose his father had
heard him getting in at the window and had come down and
shot him for a burglar? Then, again, suppose his father had
come down, pistol in hand, and he had cried out in time to
save himself, and his father had been horrified to think how
nearly he had killed him? Then, again, suppose a day should
come when his father would remember that night, and wish
there had been no warning cry to stay his hand? With this
last supposition Paul entertained himself until daybreak.

The following Sunday was fine; the sodden November
chill was broken by the last flash of autumnal summer. In
the morning Paul had to go to church and Sabbath school,
as always. On seasonable Sunday afternoons the burghers of
Cordelia Street usually sat out on their front "stoops," and
talked to their neighbors on the next stoop, or called to those
across the street in neighborly fashion. The men sat placidly
on gay cushions placed upon the steps that led down to the
sidewalk, while the women, in their Sunday "waists," sat in
rockers on the cramped porches, pretending to be greatly at
their ease. The children played in the streets; there were so
many of them that the place resembled the recreation grounds

of a kindergarten. The men on the steps—all in their shirt sleeves, their vests unbuttoned—sat with their legs well apart, their stomachs comfortably protruding, and talked of the prices of things, or told anecdotes of the sagacity of their various chiefs and overlords. They occasionally looked over the multitude of squabbling children, listened affectionately to their high-pitched, nasal voices, smiling to see their own proclivities reproduced in their offspring, and interspersed their legends of the iron kings with remarks about their sons' progress at school, their grades in arithmetic, and the amounts they had saved in their toy banks.

On this last Sunday of November, Paul sat all the afternoon on the lowest step of his "stoop," staring into the street, while his sisters, in their rockers, were talking to the minister's daughters next door about how many shirtwaists they had made in the last week, and how many waffles some one had eaten at the last church supper. When the weather was warm, and his father was in a particularly jovial frame of mind, the girls made lemonade, which was always brought out in a red-glass pitcher, ornamented with forget-me-nots in blue enamel. This the girls thought very fine, and the neighbors joked about the suspicious colour of the pitcher.

Today Paul's father, on the top step, was talking to a young man who shifted a restless baby from knee to knee. He happened to be the young man who was daily held up to Paul as a model, and after whom it was his father's dearest hope that he would pattern. This young man was of a ruddy complexion, with a compressed, red mouth, and faded, near-sighted eyes, over which he wore thick spectacles, with gold bows that curved about his ears. He was clerk to one of the magnates of a great steel corporation, and was looked upon in Cordelia Street as a young man with a future. There was a story that, some five years ago—he was now barely twenty-six—he had been a trifle "dissipated," but in order to curb his appetites and save the loss of time and strength that a sowing of wild oats might have entailed, he had taken his chief's advice, oft reiterated to his employes, and at twenty-one had married the first woman whom he could persuade to share his fortunes. She happened to be an angular school-mistress, much older than he, who also wore thick glasses, and who had now borne him four children, all nearsighted, like herself.

The young man was relating how his chief, now cruising in the Mediterranean, kept in touch with all the details of the business, arranging his office hours on his yacht just as though he were at home, and "knocking off work enough to keep two stenographers busy." His father told, in turn, the plan his corporation was considering, of putting in an electric railway plant at Cairo. Paul snapped his teeth; he had an awful apprehension that they might spoil it all before he got there. Yet he rather liked to hear these legends of the iron kings, that were told and retold on Sundays and holidays; these stories of palaces in Venice, yachts on the Mediterranean, and high play at Monte Carlo appealed to his fancy, and he was interested in the triumphs of cash boys who had become famous, though he had no mind for the cash-boy stage.

After supper was over, and he had helped to dry the dishes, Paul nervously asked his father whether he could go to George's to get some help in his geometry, and still more nervously asked for carfare. This latter request he had to repeat, as his father, on principle, did not like to hear requests for money, whether much or little. He asked Paul whether he could not go to some boy who lived nearer, and told him that he ought not to leave his schoolwork until Sunday; but he gave him the dime. He was not a poor man, but he had a worthy ambition to come up in the world. His only reason for allowing Paul to usher was that he thought a boy ought to be earning a little.

Paul bounded upstairs, scrubbed the greasy odor of the dishwater from his hands with the ill-smelling soap he hated, and then shook over his fingers a few drops of violet water from the bottle he kept hidden in his drawer. He left the house with his geometry conspicuously under his arm, and the moment he got out of Cordelia Street and boarded a downtown car, he shook off the lethargy of two deadening days, and began to live again.

The leading juvenile of the permanent stock company which played at one of the downtown theatres was an acquaintance of Paul's, and the boy had been invited to drop in at the Sunday night rehearsals whenever he could. For more than a year Paul had spent every available moment loitering about Charley Edwards's dressing room. He had won a place among Edwards's following not only because the young actor, who could not afford to employ a dresser, often found him useful, but because he recognized in Paul something akin to what churchmen term "vocation."

It was at the theatre and at Carnegie Hall that Paul really lived; the rest was but a sleep and a forgetting. This was Paul's fairy tale, and it had for him all the allurement of a secret love. The moment he inhaled the gassy, painty, dusty odor behind the scenes, he breathed like a prisoner set free, and felt within him the possibility of doing or saying splendid, brilliant things. The moment the cracked orchestra beat out the overture from *Martha*, or jerked at the serenade from *Rigoletto*, all stupid and ugly things slid from him, and his senses were deliciously, yet delicately fired.

Perhaps it was because, in Paul's world, the natural

nearly always wore the guise of ugliness, that a certain element of artificiality seemed to him necessary in beauty. Perhaps it was because his experience of life elsewhere was so full of Sabbath-school picnics, petty economies, wholesome advice as to how to succeed in life, and the unescapable odors of cooking, that he found this existence so alluring, these smartly clad men and women so attractive, that he was so moved by these starry apple orchards that bloomed perennially under the limelight.

It would be difficult to put it strongly enough how convincingly the stage entrance of that theatre was for Paul the actual portal of Romance. Certainly none of the company ever suspected it, least of all Charley Edwards. It was very like the old stories that used to float about London of fabulously rich Jews, who had subterranean halls, with palms, and fountains, and soft lamps and richly apparelled women who never saw the disenchanting light of·London day. So, in the midst of that smoke-palled city, enamoured of figures and grimy toil, Paul had his secret temple, his wishing-carpet, his bit of blue-and-white Mediterranean shore bathed in perpetual sunshine.

Several of Paul's teachers had a theory that his imagination had been perverted by garish fiction; but the truth was, he scarcely ever read at all. The books at home were not such as would either tempt or corrupt a youthful mind, and as for reading the novels that some of his friends urged upon him—well, he got what he wanted much more quickly from music; any sort of music, from an orchestra to a barrel organ. He needed only the spark, the indescribable thrill that made his imagination master of his senses, and he could make plots and pictures enough of his own. It was equally true that he was not stage-struck—not, at any rate, in the usual acceptation of that expression. He had no desire to become an actor, any more than he had to become a musician. He felt no necessity to do any of these things; what he wanted was to see, to be in the atmosphere, float on the wave of it, to be carried out, blue league after blue league, away from everything.

After a night behind the scenes, Paul found the schoolroom more than ever repulsive; the hard floors and naked walls; the prosy men who never wore frock coats, or violets in their buttonholes; the women with their dull gowns, shrill voices, and pitiful seriousness about prepositions that govern the dative. He could not bear to have the other pupils think, for a moment, that he took these people seriously; he must convey to them that he considered it all trivial, and was there only by way of a joke, anyway. He had autographed pictures of all the members of the stock company, which he showed his classmates, telling them the most incredible stories of his familiarity with these people, of his acquaintance with the soloists who came to Carnegie Hall, his suppers with them and the flowers he sent them. When these stories lost their effect, and his audience grew listless, he would bid all the boys good-bye, announcing that he was going to travel for a while, going to Naples, to California, to Egypt. Then, next Monday, he would slip back, conscious and nervously smiling; his sister was ill, and he would have to defer his voyage until spring.

Matters went steadily worse with Paul at school. In the itch to let his instructors know how heartily he despised them, and how thoroughly he was appreciated elsewhere, he mentioned once or twice that he had no time to fool with theorems, adding—with a twitch of the eyebrows and a touch of that nervous bravado which so perplexed them—that he was helping the people down at the stock company; they were old friends of his.

The upshot of the matter was that the Principal went to Paul's father, and Paul was taken out of school and put to work. The manager at Carnegie Hall was told to get another usher in his stead; the doorkeeper at the theatre was warned not to admit him to the house; and Charley Edwards remorsefully promised the boy's father not to see him again.

The members of the stock company were vastly amused when some of Paul's stories reached them—especially the women. They were hard-working women, most of them supporting indolent husbands or brothers, and they laughed rather bitterly at having stirred the boy to such fervid and florid inventions. They agreed with the faculty and with his father, that Paul's was a bad case.

The east-bound train was ploughing through a January snowstorm; the dull dawn was beginning to show gray when the engine whistled a mile out of Newark. Paul started up from the seat where he had lain curled in uneasy slumber, rubbed the breath-misted window glass with his hand, and peered out. The snow was whirling in curling eddies above the white bottom lands, and the drifts lay already deep in the fields and along the fences, while here and there the long dead grass and dried weed stalks protruded black above it. Lights shone from the scattered houses, and a gang of laborers who stood beside the track waved their lanterns.

Paul had slept very little, and he felt grimy and uncomfortable. He had made the all-night journey in a day coach because he was afraid if he took a Pullman he might be seen by some Pittsburgh businessman who had noticed him in Denny & Carson's office. When the whistle woke him, he clutched quickly at his breast pocket, glancing about him

with an uncertain smile. But the little, clay-bespattered
Italians were still sleeping, the slatternly women across the
aisle were in open-mouthed oblivion, and even the crumby,
crying babies were for the nonce stilled. Paul settled back to
struggle with his impatience as best he could.

When he arrived at the Jersey City Station, he hurried
through his breakfast, manifestly ill at ease and keeping a
sharp eye about him. After he reached the Twenty-third
Street Station, he consulted a cabman, and had himself driven
to a men's furnishing establishment which was just opening
for the day. He spent upward of two hours there, buying
with endless reconsidering and great care. His new street suit
he put on in the fitting room; the frock coat and dress clothes
he had bundled into the cab with his new shirts. Then he
drove to a hatter's and a shoe house. His next errand was at
Tiffany's, where he selected silver-mounted brushes and a
scarf pin. He would not wait to have his silver marked, he
said. Lastly, he stopped at a trunk shop on Broadway, and
had his purchases packed into various travelling bags.

It was a little after one o'clock when he drove up to
the Waldorf, and, after settling with the cabman, went into
the office. He registered from Washington, said his mother
and father had been abroad, and that he had come down to
await the arrival of their steamer. He told his story plausibly
and had no trouble, since he offered to pay for them in advance, in engaging his rooms: a sleeping room, sitting room
and bath.

Not once, but a hundred times Paul had planned this
entry into New York. He had gone over every detail of it
with Charley Edwards, and in his scrapbook at home there
were pages of description about New York hotels, cut from
the Sunday papers.

When he was shown to his sitting room on the eighth

floor, he saw at a glance that everything was as it should be; there was but one detail in his mental picture that the place did not realize, so he rang for the bell boy and sent him down for flowers. He moved about nervously until the boy returned, putting away his new linen and fingering it delightedly as he did so. When the flowers came, he put them hastily into water, and then tumbled into a hot bath. Presently he came out of his white bathroom, resplendent in his new silk underwear, and playing with the tassels of his red robe. The snow was whirling so fiercely outside his windows that he could scarcely see across the street; but within, the air was deliciously soft and fragrant. He put the violets and jonquils on the taboret beside the couch, and threw himself down with a long sigh, covering himself with a Roman blanket. He was thoroughly tired; he had been in such haste, he had stood up to such a strain, covered so much ground in the last twenty-four hours, that he wanted to think how it had all come about. Lulled by the sound of the wind, the warm air, and the cool fragrance of the flowers, he sank into deep, drowsy retrospection.

It had been wonderfully simple; when they had shut him out of the theatre and concert hall, when they had taken away his bone, the whole thing was virtually determined. The rest was a mere matter of opportunity. The only thing that at all surprised him was his own courage—for he realized well enough that he had always been tormented by fear, a sort of apprehensive dread that, of late years, as the meshes of the lies he had told closed about him, had been pulling the muscles of his body tighter and tighter. Until now, he could not remember a time when he had not been dreading something. Even when he was a little boy, it was always there—behind him, or before, or on either side. There had always been the shadowed corner, the dark place into which he dared not look, but from which something seemed always to be watching him—and Paul had done things that were not pretty to watch, he knew.

But now he had a curious sense of relief, as though he had at last thrown down the gauntlet to the thing in the corner.

Yet it was but a day since he had been sulking in the traces; but yesterday afternoon that he had been sent to the bank with Denny & Carson's deposit as usual—but this time he was instructed to leave the book to be balanced. There was above two thousand dollars in checks, and nearly a thousand in the bank notes which he had taken from the book and quietly transferred to his pocket. At the bank he had made out a new deposit slip. His nerves had been steady enough to permit of his returning to the office, where he had finished his work and asked for a full day's holiday tomorrow, Saturday, giving a perfectly reasonable pretext. The bankbook, he knew, would not be returned before Monday or Tuesday, and his father would be out of town for the next week. From the time he slipped the bank notes into his pocket until he boarded the night train for New York, he had not known a moment's hesitation.

How astonishingly easy it had all been; here he was, the thing done; and this time there would be no awakening, no figure at the top of the stairs. He watched the snow flakes whirling by his window until he fell asleep.

When he awoke, it was four o'clock in the afternoon. He bounded up with a start; one of his precious days gone already! He spent nearly an hour in dressing, watching every stage of his toilet carefully in the mirror. Everything was quite perfect; he was exactly the kind of boy he had always wanted to be.

When he went downstairs, Paul took a carriage and

drove up Fifth Avenue toward the Park. The snow had somewhat abated; carriages and tradesmen's wagons were hurrying soundlessly to and fro in the winter twilight; boys in
woollen mufflers were shovelling off the doorsteps; the
avenue stages made fine spots of color against the white
street. Here and there on the corners were stands, with whole
flower gardens blooming behind glass windows, against
which the snowflakes stuck and melted; violets, roses, carnations, lilies of the valley—somehow vastly more lovely and
alluring that they blossomed thus unnaturally in the snow.
The Park itself was a wonderful stage winter piece.

When he returned, the pause of the twilight had
ceased, and the tune on the streets had changed. The snow
was falling faster, lights streamed from the hotels that reared
their many stories fearlessly up into the storm, defying the
raging Atlantic winds. A long black stream of carriages
poured down the avenue, intersected here and there by other
streams, tending horizontally. There were a score of cabs
about the entrance of his hotel, and his driver had to wait.
Boys in livery were running in and out of the awning
stretched across the sidewalk, up and down the red velvet
carpet laid from the door to the street. Above, about, within
it all, was the rumble and roar, the hurry and toss of
thousands of human beings as hot for pleasure as himself,
and on every side of him towered the glaring affirmation of
the omnipotence of wealth.

The boy set his teeth and drew his shoulders together
in a spasm of realization; the plot of all dramas, the text of all
romances, the nerve stuff of all sensations were whirling
about him like the snowflakes. He burnt like a faggot in a
tempest.

When Paul came down to dinner, the music of the

orchestra floated up the elevator shaft to greet him. As he stepped into the thronged corridor, he sank back into one of the chairs against the wall to get his breath. The lights, the chatter, the perfumes, the bewildering medley of color— he had, for a moment, the feeling of not being able to stand it. But only for a moment; these were his own people, he told himself. He went slowly about the corridors through the writing rooms, smoking rooms, reception rooms, as though he were exploring the chambers of an enchanted palace, built and peopled for him alone.

When he reached the dining room he sat down at a table near a window. The flowers, the white linen, the many-colored wine glasses, the gay toilettes of the women, the low popping of corks, the undulating repetitions of the *Blue Danube* from the orchestra, all flooded Paul's dream with bewildering radiance. When the roseate tinge of his champagne was added—that cold, precious bubbling stuff that creamed and foamed in his glass—Paul wondered that there were honest men in the world at all. This was what all the world was fighting for, he reflected; this was what all the struggle was about. He doubted the reality of his past. Had he ever known a place called Cordelia Street, a place where fagged-looking businessmen boarded the early car? Mere rivets in a machine they seemed to Paul,—sickening men, with combings of children's hair always hanging to their coats, and the smell of cooking in their clothes. Cordelia Street—Ah, that belonged to another time and country! Had he not always been thus, had he not sat here night after night, from as far back as he could remember, looking pensively over just such shimmering textures, and slowly twirling the stem of a glass like this one between his thumb and middle finger? He rather thought he had.

He was not in the least abashed or lonely. He had no especial desire to meet or to know any of these people; all he demanded was the right to look on and conjecture, to watch the pageant. The mere stage properties were all he contended for. Nor was he lonely later in the evening, in his loge at the Opera. He was entirely rid of his nervous misgivings, of his forced aggressiveness, of the imperative desire to show himself different from his surroundings. He felt now that his surroundings explained him. Nobody questioned his purple; he had only to wear it passively. He had only to glance down at his dress coat to reassure himself that here it would be impossible for any one to humiliate him.

He found it hard to leave his beautiful sitting room to go to bed that night, and sat long watching the raging storm from his turret window. When he went to sleep, it was with the lights turned on in his bedroom, partly because of his old timidity, and partly so that, if he should wake in the night, there would be no wretched moment of doubt, no horrible suspicion of yellow wallpaper, or of Washington and Calvin above his bed.

On Sunday morning the city was practically snowbound. Paul breakfasted late, and in the afternoon he fell in with a wild San Francisco boy, a freshman at Yale, who said he had run down for a "little flyer" over Sunday. The young man offered to show Paul the night side of the town, and the two boys went off together after dinner, not returning to the hotel until seven o'clock the next morning. They had started out in the confiding warmth of a champagne friendship, but their parting in the elevator was singularly cool. The freshman pulled himself together to make his train, and Paul went to bed. He awoke at two o'clock in the afternoon, very thirsty and dizzy, and rang for ice water, coffee, and the Pittsburgh papers.

On the part of the hotel management, Paul excited no suspicion. There was this to be said for him, that he wore his spoils with dignity and in no way made himself conspicuous. His chief greediness lay in his ears and eyes, and his excesses were not offensive ones. His dearest pleasures were the gray winter twilights in his sitting room, his quiet enjoyment of his flowers, his clothes, his wide divan, his cigarette and his sense of power. He could not remember a time when he had felt so at peace with himself. The mere release from the necessity of petty lying, lying every day and every day, restored his self-respect. He had never lied for pleasure, even at school; but to make himself noticed and admired, to assert his difference from other Cordelia Street boys; and he felt a good deal more manly, more honest, even, now that he had no need for boastful pretensions, now that he could, as his actor friends used to say, "dress the part." It was characteristic that remorse did not occur to him. His golden days went by without a shadow, and he made each as perfect as he could.

On the eighth day after his arrival in New York, he found the whole affair exploited in the Pittsburgh papers, exploited with a wealth of detail which indicated that local news of a sensational nature was at a low ebb. The firm of Denny & Carson announced that the boy's father had refunded the full amount of his theft, and that they had no intention of prosecuting. The Cumberland minister had been interviewed, and expressed his hope of yet reclaiming the motherless lad, and Paul's Sabbath-school teacher declared that she would spare no effort to that end. The rumor had reached Pittsburgh that the boy had been seen in a New York hotel, and his father had gone East to find him and bring him home.

Paul had just come in to dress for dinner; he sank into a chair, weak in the knees, and clasped his head in his hands. It was to be worse than jail, even; the tepid waters of Cordelia Street were to close over him finally and forever. The gray monotony stretched before him in hopeless, unrelieved years; Sabbath school, Young People's Meeting, the yellow-papered room, the damp dish towels; it all rushed back upon him with sickening vividness. He had the old feeling that the orchestra had suddenly stopped, the sinking sensation that the play was over. The sweat broke out on his face, and he sprang to his feet, looked about him with his white, conscious smile, and winked at himself in the mirror. With something of the childish belief in miracles with which he had so often gone to class, all his lessons unlearned, Paul dressed and dashed whistling down the corridor to the elevator.

He had no sooner entered the dining room and caught the measure of the music than his remembrance was lightened by his old elastic power of claiming the moment, mounting with it, and finding it all sufficient. The glare and glitter about him, the mere scenic accessories had again, and for the last time, their old potency. He would show himself that he was game, he would finish the thing splendidly. He doubted, more than ever, the existence of Cordelia Street, and for the first time he drank his wine recklessly. Was he not, after all, one of these fortunate beings? Was he not still himself, and in his own place? He drummed a nervous accompaniment to the music and looked about him, telling himself over and over that it had paid.

He reflected drowsily, to the swell of the violin and

the chill sweetness of his wine, that he might have done it more wisely. He might have caught an outbound steamer and been well out of their clutches before now. But the other side of the world had seemed too far away and too uncertain then; he could not have waited for it; his need had been too sharp. If he had to choose over again, he would do the same thing tomorrow. He looked affectionately about the dining room, now gilded with a soft mist. Ah, it had paid indeed!

Paul was awakened next morning by a painful throbbing in his head and feet. He had thrown himself across the bed without undressing, and had slept with his shoes on. His limbs and hands were lead-heavy, and his tongue and throat were parched. There came upon him one of those fateful attacks of clear-headedness that never occurred except when he was physically exhausted and his nerves hung loose. He lay still and closed his eyes and let the tide of realities wash over him.

His father was in New York; "stopping at some joint or other," he told himself. The memory of successive summers on the front stoop fell upon him like a weight of black water. He had not a hundred dollars left; and he knew now, more than ever, that money was everything, the wall that stood between all he loathed and all he wanted. The thing was winding itself up; he had thought of that on his first glorious day in New York, and had even provided a way to snap the thread. It lay on his dressing table now; he had got it out last night when he came blindly up from dinner,—but the shiny metal hurt his eyes, and he disliked the look of it, anyway.

He rose and moved about with a painful effort, succumbing now and again to attacks of nausea. It was the old depression exaggerated; all the world had become Cordelia

Street. Yet somehow he was not afraid of anything, was absolutely calm; perhaps because he had looked into the dark corner at last, and knew. It was bad enough, what he saw there; but somehow not so bad as his long fear of it had been. He saw everything clearly now. He had a feeling that he had made the best of it, that he had lived the sort of life he was meant to live, and for half an hour he sat staring at the revolver. But he told himself that was not the way, so he went downstairs and took a cab to the ferry.

When Paul arrived at Newark, he got off the train and took another cab, directing the driver to follow the Pennsylvania tracks out of the town. The snow lay heavy on the roadways and had drifted deep in the open fields. Only here and there the dead grass or dried weed stalks projected, singularly black, above it. Once well into the country, Paul dismissed the carriage and walked, floundering along the tracks, his mind a medley of irrelevant things. He seemed to hold in his brain an actual picture of everything he had seen that morning. He remembered every feature of both his drivers, the toothless old woman from whom he had bought the red flowers in his coat, the agent from whom he had got his ticket, and all of his fellow-passengers on the ferry. His mind, unable to cope with vital matters near at hand, worked feverishly and deftly at sorting and grouping these images. They made for him a part of the ugliness of the world, of the ache in his head, and the bitter burning on his tongue. He stopped and put a handful of snow into his mouth as he walked, but that, too, seemed hot. When he reached a little hillside, where the tracks ran through a cut some twenty feet below him, he stopped and sat down.

The carnations in his coat were drooping with the cold, he noticed; all their red glory over. It occurred to him that all the flowers he had seen in the show windows that first night must have gone the same way, long before this. It was only one splendid breath they had, in spite of their brave mockery at the winter outside the glass. It was a losing game in the end, it seemed, this revolt against the homilies by which the world is run. Paul took one of the blossoms carefully from his coat and scooped a little hole in the snow, where he covered it up. Then he dozed a while, from his weak condition, seeming insensible to the cold.

The sound of an approaching train woke him, and he started to his feet, remembering only his resolution, and afraid lest he should be too late. He stood watching the approaching locomotive, his teeth chattering, his lips drawn away from them in a frightened smile; once or twice he glanced nervously sidewise, as though he were being watched. When the right moment came, he jumped. As he fell, the folly of his haste occurred to him with merciless clearness, the vastness of what he had left undone. There flashed through his brain, clearer than ever before, the blue of Adriatic water, the yellow of Algerian sands.

He felt something strike his chest—his body was being thrown swiftly through the air, on and on, immeasurably far and fast, while his limbs gently relaxed. Then, because the picture-making mechanism was crushed, the disturbing visions flashed into black, and Paul dropped back into the immense design of things.

Booth Tarkington (1869-1946)

*Born in Indianapolis, Booth Tarkington attended Pur-
due for a brief period and was graduated from Princeton.
In his short stories and novels he presents a balanced picture of middle-class life in Indiana. The humorous and
tragic aspects of life at different social strata are depicted by
this author, who received Pulitzer Prizes for* The Magnificent
Ambersons *(1919) and* Alice Adams *(1922). The latter novel
pictures an attractive young lady, who, conforming to middle-
class conventions, tries desperately to attain social position.
Tarkington reveals her dreams of success and her awareness
of the realities. Popular at sixteen, fading at twenty, Alice
experiences an unhappiness summed up in the final line of the
preceding chapter: "She had been a belle too soon."*

ALICE ADAMS

CHAPTER 8

The device of the absentee partner has the defect that
it cannot be employed for longer than ten or fifteen minutes
at a time, and it may not be repeated more than twice in one
evening: a single repetition, indeed, is weak, and may prove

a betrayal. Alice knew that her present performance could be effective during only this interval between dances; and though her eyes were guarded, she anxiously counted over the partnerless young men who lounged together in the doorways within her view. Every one of them ought to have asked her for dances, she thought, and although she might have been put to it to give a reason why any of them "ought," her heart was hot with resentment against them.

For a girl who has been a belle, it is harder to live through these bad times than it is for one who has never known anything better. Like a figure of painted and brightly varnished wood, Ella Dowling sat against the wall through dance after dance with glassy imperturbability; it was easier to be wooden, Alice thought, if you had your mother with you, as Ella had. You were left with at least the shred of a pretense that you came to sit with your mother as a spectator, and not to offer yourself to be danced with by men who looked you over and rejected you—not for the first time. "Not for the first time": there lay a sting! Why had you thought this time might be different from the other times? Why had you broken your back picking those hundreds of violets?

Hating the fatuous young men in the doorways more bitterly for every instant that she had to maintain her tableau, the smiling Alice knew fierce impulses to spring to her feet and shout at them, "You *idiots!*" Hands in pockets they lounged against the pilasters, or faced one another, laughing vaguely, each one of them seeming to Alice no more than so much mean beef in clothes. She wanted to tell them they were no better than that; and it seemed a cruel thing of heaven to let them go on believing themselves young lords. They were doing nothing, killing time. Wasn't she at her lowest value at least a means of killing time? Evidently the mean beeves thought not. And when one of them finally lounged across the corridor and spoke to her, he was the very one to whom she preferred her loneliness.

"Waiting for somebody, Lady Alicia?" he asked negligently; and his easy burlesque of her name was like the familiarity of the rest of him. He was one of those full-bodied, grossly handsome men who are powerful and active, but never submit themselves to the rigour of becoming athletes, though they shoot and fish from expensive camps. Gloss is the most shining outward mark of the type. Nowadays these men no longer use brilliantine on their moustaches, but they have gloss bought from manicure-girls, from masseurs, and from automobile-makers; and their eyes, usually large, are glossy. None of this is allowed to interfere with business; these are "good business men." and often make large fortunes. They are men of imagination about two things —women and money, and, combining their imaginings about both, usually make a wise first marriage. Later, however, they are apt to imagine too much about some little woman without whom life seems duller than need be. They run away, leaving the first wife well enough dowered. They are never intentionally unkind to women, and in the end they usually make the mistake of thinking they have had their money's worth of life. Here was Mr. Harvey Malone, a young specimen in an earlier stage of development, trying to marry Henrietta Lamb, and now sauntering over to speak to Alice, as a time-killer before his next dance with Henrietta.

Alice made no response to his question, and he dropped lazily into the vacant chair, from which she sharply withdrew her hand. "I might as well use his chair till he comes, don't you think? You don't *mind*, do you, old girl?"

"Oh, no," Alice said. "It doesn't matter one way or the other. Please don't call me that."

"So that's how you feel?" Mr. Malone laughed indulgently, without much interest. "I've been meaning to come to see you for a long time—honestly I have—because I wanted to have a good talk with you about old times. I know you think it was funny, after the way I used to come to your house two or three times a week, and sometimes oftener—well, I don't blame you for being hurt, the way I stopped without explaining or anything. The truth is there wasn't any reason. I just happened to have a lot of important things to do and couldn't find the time. But I *am* going to call on you some evening—honestly I am. I don't wonder you think—"

"You're mistaken," Alice said. "I've never thought anything about it at all."

"Well, well!" he said, and looked at her languidly. "What's the use of being cross with this old man? He always means well." And, extending his arm, he would have given her a friendly pat upon the shoulder but she evaded it. "Well, well!" he said. "Seems to me you're getting awful tetchy! Don't you like your old friends any more?"

"Not all of them."

"Who's the new one?" he asked, teasingly. "Come on and tell us, Alice. Who is it you were holding this chair for?"

"Never mind."

"Well, all I've got to do is to sit here till he comes back; then I'll see who it is."

"He may not come back before you have to go."

"Guess you got me *that* time," Malone admitted, laughing as he rose. "They're tuning up, and I've got this dance. I *am* coming around to see you some evening." He moved away, calling back over his shoulder, "Honestly, I am!"

Alice did not look at him.

She had held her tableau as long as she could; it was time for her to abandon the box trees; and she stepped forth frowning, as if a little annoyed with the absentee for being such a time upon her errand; whereupon the two chairs were instantly seized by a coquetting pair who intended to "sit out" the dance. She walked quickly down the broad corridor, turned into the broader hall, and hurriedly entered the dressing room where she had left her wraps.

She stayed here as long as she could, pretending to arrange her hair at a mirror, then fidgeting with one of her slipper buckles; but the intelligent elderly woman in charge of the room made an indefinite sojourn impracticable. "Perhaps I could help you with that buckle, Miss," she suggested, approaching. "Has it come loose?" Alice wrenched desperately; then it was loose. The competent woman, producing needle and thread, deftly made the buckle fast; and there was nothing for Alice to do but to express her gratitude and go.

She went to the door of the cloakroom opposite, where a coloured man stood watchfully in the doorway. "I wonder if you know which of the gentlemen is my brother, Mr. Walter Adams," she said.

"Yes'm; I know him."

"Could you tell me where he is?"

"No'm; I couldn't say."

"Well, if you see him, would you please tell him that his sister, Miss Adams, is looking for him and very anxious to speak to him?"

"Yes'm. Sho'ly, sho'ly!"

As she went away he stared after her and seemed to swell with some bursting emotion. In fact, it was too much for him, and he suddenly retired within the room, releasing strangulated laughter.

Walter remonstrated. Behind an excellent screen of coats and hats, in a remote part of the room, he was kneeling on the floor, engaged in a game of chance with a second coloured attendant; and the laughter became so vehement that it not only interfered with the pastime in hand, but threatened to attract frozen-face attention.

"I cain' he'p it, man," the laughter explained. "I cain' he'p it! You sut'n'y the beatin'es' white boy 'n 'is city!"

The dancers were swinging into an "encore" as Alice halted for an irresolute moment in a doorway. Across the room, a cluster of matrons sat chatting absently, their eyes on their dancing daughters; and Alice, finding a refugee's courage, dodged through the scurrying couples, seated herself in a chair on the outskirts of this colony of elders, and began to talk eagerly to the matron nearest her. The matron seemed unaccustomed to so much vivacity, and responded but dryly, whereupon Alice was more vivacious than ever; for she meant now to present the picture of a jolly girl too much interested in these wise older women to bother about every foolish young man who asked her for a dance.

Her matron was constrained to go so far as to supply a tolerant nod, now and then, in complement to the girl's animation, and Alice was grateful for the nods. In this fashion she supplemented the exhausted resources of the dressing room and the box-tree nook; and lived through two more dances, when again Mr. Frank Dowling presented himself as a partner.

She needed no pretense to seek the dressing room for repairs after that number; this time they were necessary and genuine. Dowling waited for her, and when she came out he explained for the fourth or fifth time how the accident had happened. "It was entirely those other people's fault," he said. "They got me in a kind of corner, because neither of those fellows knows the least thing about guiding; they just jam ahead and expect everybody to get out of *their* way. It was Charlotte Thom's diamond crescent pin that got caught on your dress in the back and made such a—"

"Never mind," Alice said in a tired voice. "The maid fixed it so that she says it isn't very noticeable."

"Well, it isn't," he returned. "You could hardly tell there'd been anything the matter. Where do you want to go? Mother's been interfering in my affairs some more and I've got the next taken."

"I was sitting with Mrs. George Dresser. You might take me back there."

He left her with the matron, and Alice returned to her picture-making, so that once more, while two numbers passed, whoever cared to look was offered the sketch of a jolly, clever girl preoccupied with her elders. Then she found her friend Mildred standing before her, presenting Mr. Arthur Russell, who asked her to dance with him.

Alice looked uncertain, as though not sure what her engagements were; but her perplexity cleared; she nodded, and swung rhythmically away with the tall applicant. She was not grateful to her hostess for this alms. What a young hostess does with a fiancé, Alice thought, is to make him dance with the unpopular girls. She supposed that Mr. Arthur Russell had already danced with Ella Dowling.

The loan of a lover, under these circumstances, may be painful to the lessee, and Alice, smiling never more brightly, found nothing to say to Mr. Russell, though she thought he might have found something to say to her. "I wonder what Mildred told him," she thought. "Probably she said, 'Dearest, there's one more girl you've got to help me out with. You wouldn't like her much, but she dances well enough and she's having a rotten time. Nobody ever goes near her any more.' "

When the music stopped Russell added his applause to the hand-clapping that encouraged the uproarious instruments to continue, and as they renewed the tumult, he said heartily, "That's splendid!"

Alice gave him a glance, necessarily at short range, and found his eyes kindly and pleased. Here was a friendly soul, it appeared, who probably "liked everybody." No doubt he had applauded for an "encore" when he danced with Ella Dowling, gave Ella the same genial look, and said, "That's splendid!"

When the "encore" was over, Alice spoke to him for the first time.

"Mildred will be looking for you," she said. "I think you'd better take me back to where you found me."

He looked surprised. "Oh, if you—"

"I'm sure Mildred will be needing you," Alice said, and as she took his arm and they walked toward Mrs. Dresser, she thought it might be just possible to make a further use of the loan. "Oh, I wonder if you—" she began.

"Yes?" he said, quickly.

"You don't know my brother, Walter Adams," she said. "But he's somewhere—I think possibly he's in the smoking room or some place where girls aren't expected, and if you wouldn't think it too much trouble to inquire—"

"I'll find him," Russell said, promptly. "Thank you so much for that dance. I'll bring your brother in a moment."

It was to be a long moment, Alice decided, presently. Mrs. Dresser had grown restive; and her nods and vague responses to her young dependent's gaieties were as meager as they could well be. Evidently the matron had no intention of appearing to her world in the light of a chaperone for Alice Adams; and she finally made this clear. With a word or two of excuse, breaking into something Alice was saying, she rose and went to sit next to Mildred's mother, who had become the nucleus of the cluster. So Alice was left very much against the wall, with short stretches of vacant chairs on each side of her. She had come to the end of her picture-making, and could only pretend that there was something amusing the matter with the arm of her chair.

She supposed that Mildred's Mr. Russell had forgotten Walter by this time. "I'm not even an intimate enough friend of Mildred's for him to have thought he ought to bother to tell me he couldn't find him," she thought. And then she saw Russell coming across the room toward her, with Walter beside him. She jumped up gaily.

"Oh, thank you!" she cried, "I know this naughty boy must have been terribly hard to find. Mildred'll *never* forgive me! I've put you to so much—"

"Not at all," he said, amiably, and went away, leaving the brother and sister together.

"Walter, let's dance just once more," Alice said, touching his arm placatively. " I thought—well, perhaps we might go home then."

But Walter's expression was that of a person upon whom an outrage had just been perpetrated. "No," he said. "We've stayed *this* long. I'm goin' to wait and see what they got to eat. And you look here!" He turned upon her angrily. "Don't you ever do that again!"

"Do what?"

"Send somebody after me that pokes his nose into every corner of the house till he finds me! 'Are you Mr. Walter Adams?' he says. I guess he must asked everybody in the place if they were Mr. Walter Adams! Well, I'll bet a few iron men you wouldn't send anybody to hunt for me again if you knew where he found me!"

"Where was it?"

Walter decided that her fit punishment was to know. "I was shootin' dice in the cloakroom."

"And he *saw* you?"

"Unless he was blind!" said Walter. "Come on, I'll dance this one more dance with you. Supper comes after that, and *then* we'll go home."

Mrs. Adams heard Alice's key turning in the front door and hurried down the stairs to meet her.

"Did you get wet coming in, darling?" she asked. "Did you have a good time?"

"Just lovely!" Alice said cheerily; and after she had arranged the latch for Walter, who had gone to return the little car, she followed her mother upstairs and hummed a dance tune on the way.

"Oh, I'm so glad you had a nice time," Mrs. Adams said, as they reached the door of her daughter's room together. "You *deserved* to, and it's lovely to think—"

But at this, without warning. Alice threw herself into her mother's arms, sobbing so loudly that in his room, close by, her father, half drowsing through the night, started to full wakefulness.

Ernest Hemingway (1899–1961)

Ernest Hemingway was born in Oak Park, Illinois. He worked on a Kansas City newspaper in his early professional life, served as an ambulance driver on the Italian front during World War I and was wounded. Hemingway was awarded the Nobel Prize in Literature (1954). In his novels and short stories he relied on a simple style, short, clipped sentences, brief descriptions, staccato conversations, colloquial language and understatement. A member of the "hardboiled" school in American literature, Ernest Hemingway through his realistic writing expressed the "Lost Generation" disillusionment, a fatalistic attitude, and a sense of futility about life in the post-World War I era.

SOLDIER'S HOME

Krebs went to the war from a Methodist college in Kansas. There is a picture which shows him among his fraternity brothers, all of them wearing exactly the same height and style collar. He enlisted in the Marines in 1917 and did not return to the United States until the second division returned from the Rhine in the summer of 1919.

There is a picture which shows him on the Rhine with two German girls and another corporal. Krebs and the corporal look too big for their uniforms. The German girls are not beautiful. The Rhine does not show in the picture.

By the time Krebs returned to his home town in Oklahoma the greeting of heroes was over. He came back much too late. The men from the town who had been drafted had all been welcomed elaborately on their return. There had been a great deal of hysteria. Now the reaction had set in. People seemed to think it was rather ridiculous for Krebs to be getting back so late, years after the war was over.

At first Krebs, who had been at Belleau Wood, Soissons, the Champagne, St. Mihiel and in the Argonne did not want to talk about the war at all. Later he felt the need to talk but no one wanted to hear about it. His town had heard too many atrocity stories to be thrilled by actualities. Krebs found that to be listened to at all he had to lie, and after he had done this twice he, too, had a reaction against the war and against talking about it. A distaste for everything that had happened to him in the war set in because of the lies he had told. All of the times that had been able to make him feel cool and clear inside himself when he thought of them; the times so long back when he had done the one thing, the only thing for a man to do, easily and naturally, when he might have done something else, now lost their cool, valuable quality and then were lost themselves.

His lies were quite unimportant lies and consisted in attributing to himself things other men had seen, done or heard of, and stating as facts certain apocryphal incidents familiar to all soldiers. Even his lies were not sensational at the pool room. His acquaintances, who had heard detailed accounts of German women found chained to machine guns in the Argonne forest and who could not comprehend, or were barred by their patriotism from interest in, any German machine gunners who were not chained, were not thrilled by his stories.

Krebs acquired the nausea in regard to experience that is the result of untruth or exaggeration, and when he occasionally met another man who had really been a soldier and they talked a few minutes in the dressing room at a dance he fell into the easy pose of the old soldier among other soldiers: that he had been badly, sickeningly frightened all the time. In this way he lost everything.

During this time, it was late summer, he was sleeping late in bed, getting up to walk down to the library to get a book, eating lunch at home, reading on the front porch until he became bored and then walking down through the town to spend the hottest hours of the day in the cool dark of the pool room. He loved to play pool.

In the evening he practised on his clarinet, strolled down town, read and went to bed. He was still a hero to his two young sisters. His mother would have given him breakfast in bed if he had wanted it. She often came in when he was in bed and asked him to tell her about the war, but her attention always wandered. His father was noncommittal.

Before Krebs went away to the war he had never been allowed to drive the family motor car. His father was in the real estate business and always wanted the car to be at his command when he required it to take clients out into the country to show them a piece of farm property. The car always stood outside the First National Bank building where his father had an office on the second floor. Now, after the war, it was still the same car.

Nothing was changed in the town except that the

young girls had grown up. But they lived in such a complicated world of already defined alliances and shifting feuds
that Krebs did not feel the energy or the courage to break
into it. He liked to look at them, though. There were so many
good-looking young girls. Most of them had their hair cut
short. When he went away only little girls wore their hair
like that or girls that were fast. They all wore sweaters and
shirt waists with round Dutch collars. It was a pattern. He
liked to look at them from the front porch as they walked on
the other side of the street. He liked to watch them walking
under the shade of the trees. He liked the round Dutch collars above their sweaters. He liked their silk stockings and
flat shoes. He liked their bobbed hair and the way they
walked.

When he was in town their appeal to him was not very
strong. He did not like them when he saw them in the
Greek's ice cream parlor. He did not want them themselves
really. They were too complicated. There was something else.
Vaguely he wanted a girl but he did not want to have to work
to get her. He would have liked to have a girl but he did not
want to have to spend a long time getting her. He did not
want to get into the intrigue and the politics. He did not want
to have to do any courting. He did not want to tell any more
lies. It wasn't worth it.

He did not want any consequences. He did not want
any consequences ever again. He wanted to live along without consequences. Besides he did not really need a girl. The
army had taught him that. It was all right to pose as though
you had to have a girl. Nearly everybody did that. But it
wasn't true. You did not need a girl. That was the funny
thing. First a fellow boasted how girls mean nothing to him,
that he never thought of them, that they could not touch him.

Then a fellow boasted that he could not get along without girls, that he had to have them all the time, that he could not go to sleep without them.

That was all a lie. It was all a lie both ways. You did not need a girl unless you thought about them. He learned that in the army. Then sooner or later you always got one. When you were really ripe for a girl you always got one. You did not have to think about it. Sooner or later it would come. He had learned that in the army.

Now he would have liked a girl if she had come to him and not wanted to talk. But here at home it was all too complicated. He knew he could never get through it all again. It was not worth the trouble. That was the thing about French girls and German girls. There was not all this talking. You couldn't talk much and you did not need to talk. It was simple and you were friends. He thought about France and then he began to think about Germany. On the whole he had liked Germany better. He did no want to leave Germany. He did not want to come home. Still, he had come home. He sat on the front porch.

He liked the girls that were walking along the other side of the street. He liked the look of them much better than the French girls or the German girls. But the world they were in was not the world he was in. He would like to have one of them. But it was not worth it. They were such a nice pattern. He liked the pattern. It was exciting. But he would not go through all the talking. He did not want one badly enough. He liked to look at them all, though. It was not worth it. Not now when things were getting good again.

He sat there on the porch reading a book on the war. It was a history and he was reading about all the engagements he had been in. It was the most interesting reading he had ever done. He wished there were more maps. He looked forward with a good feeling to reading all the really good histories when they would come out with good detail maps. Now he was really learning about the war. He had been a good soldier. That made a difference.

One morning after he had been home about a month his mother came into his bedroom and sat on the bed. She smoothed her apron.

"I had a talk with your father last night, Harold," she said, "and he is willing for you to take the car out in the evenings."

"Yeah?" said Krebs, who was not fully awake. "Take the car out? Yeah?"

"Yes. Your father has felt for some time that you should be able to take the car out in the evenings whenever you wished but we only talked it over last night."

"I'll bet you made him," Krebs said.

"No. It was your father's suggestion that we talk the matter over."

"Yeah. I'll bet you made him," Krebs sat up in bed.

"Will you come down to breakfast, Harold?" his mother said.

"As soon as I get my clothes on," Krebs said.

His mother went out of the room and he could hear her frying something downstairs while he washed, shaved and dressed to go down into the dining room for breakfast. While he was eating breakfast his sister brought in the mail.

"Well, Hare," she said. "You old sleepyhead. What do you ever get up for?"

Krebs looked at her. He liked her. She was his best sister.

"Have you got the paper?" he asked.

She handed him *The Kansas City Star* and he shucked off its brown wrapper and opened it to the sporting page. He folded *The Star* open and propped it against the water pitcher with his cereal dish to steady it, so he could read while he ate.

"Harold," his mother stood in the kitchen doorway, "Harold, please don't muss up the paper. Your father can't read his *Star* if it's been mussed."

"I won't muss it," Krebs said.

His sister sat down at the table and watched him while he read.

"We're playing indoor over at school this afternoon," she said. "I'm going to pitch."

"Good," said Krebs. "How's the old wing?"

"I can pitch better than lots of the boys. I tell them all you taught me. The other girls aren't much good."

"Yeah?" said Krebs.

"I tell them all you're my beau. Aren't you my beau, Hare?"

"You bet."

"Couldn't your brother really be your beau just because he's your brother?"

"I don't know."

"Sure you know. Couldn't you be my beau, Hare, if I was old enough and if you wanted to?"

"Sure. You're my girl now."

"Am I really your girl?"

"Sure."

"Do you love me?"

"Uh, huh."

"Will you love me always?"

"Sure."

"Will you come over and watch me play indoor?"

"Maybe."

"Aw, Hare, you don't love me. If you loved me, you'd want to come over and watch me play indoor."

Kreb's mother came into the dining room from the kitchen. She carried a plate with two fried eggs and some crisp bacon on it and a plate of buckwheat cakes.

"You run along, Helen," she said. "I want to talk to Harold."

She put the eggs and bacon down in front of him and brought in a jug of maple syrup for the buckwheat cakes. Then she sat down across the table from Krebs.

"I wish you'd put down the paper a minute, Harold," she said.

Krebs took down the paper and folded it.

"Have you decided what you are going to do yet, Harold?" his mother said, taking off her glasses.

"No," said Krebs.

"Don't you think it's about time?" His mother did not say this in a mean way. She seemed worried.

"I hadn't thought about it," Krebs said.

"God has some work for every one to do," his mother said. "There can be no idle hands in His Kingdom."

"I'm not in His Kingdom," Krebs said.

"We are all of us in His Kingdom."

Krebs felt embarrassed and resentful as always.

"I've worried about you so much, Harold," his mother went on. "I know the temptations you must have been exposed to. I know how weak men are. I know what your own dear grandfather, my own father, told us about the Civil War and I have prayed for you. I pray for you all day long, Harold."

Krebs looked at the bacon fat hardening on his plate.

"Your father is worried, too," his mother went on. "He thinks you have lost your ambition, that you haven't got a definite aim in life. Charley Simmons, who is just your age, has a good job and is going to be married. The boys are all settling down; they're all determined to get somewhere; you can see that boys like Charley Simmons are on their way to being really a credit to the community."

Krebs said nothing.

"Don't look that way Harold," his mother said. "You know we love you and I want to tell you for your own good how matters stand. Your father does not want to hamper your freedom. He thinks you should be allowed to drive the car. If you want to take some of the nice girls out riding with you, we are only too pleased. We want you to enjoy yourself. But you are going to have to settle down to work, Harold. Your father doesn't care what you start in at. All work is honorable as he says. But you've got to make a start at something. He asked me to speak to you this morning and then you can stop in and see him at his office."

"Is that all?" Krebs said.

"Yes. Don't you love your mother, dear boy?"

"No," Krebs said.

His mother looked at him across the table. Her eyes were shiny. She started crying.

"I don't love anybody," Krebs said.

It wasn't any good. He couldn't tell her, he couldn't make her see it. It was silly to have said it. He had only hurt her. He went over and took hold of her arms. She was crying with her head in her hands.

"I didn't mean it," he said. "I was just angry at something. I didn't mean I didn't love you."

His mother went on crying. Krebs put his arm on her shoulder.

"Can't you believe me, mother?"

His mother shook her head.

"Please, please, mother. Please believe me."

"All right," his mother said chokily. She looked up at him. "I believe you, Harold."

Krebs kissed her hair. She put her face up to him.

"I'm your mother," she said. "I held you next to my heart when you were a tiny baby."

Krebs felt sick and vaguely nauseated.

"I know, Mummy," he said. "I'll try and be a good boy for you."

"Would you kneel and pray with me, Harold?" his mother asked.

They knelt down beside the dining-room table and Kreb's mother prayed.

"Now, you pray, Harold," she said.

"I can't," Krebs said.

"Try, Harold."

"I can't."

"Do you want me to pray for you?"

"Yes."

So his mother prayed for him and then they stood up and Krebs kissed his mother and went out of the house. He had tried so to keep his life from being complicated. Still, none of it had touched him. He had felt sorry for his mother and she had made him lie. He would go to Kansas City and get a job and she would feel all right about it. There would be one more scene maybe before he got away. He would not go down to his father's office. He would miss that one. He wanted his life to go smoothly. It had just gotten going that way. Well, that was all over now, anyway. He would go over to the schoolyard and watch Helen play indoor baseball.

Dorothy Parker (1893–1968)

*Dorothy Parker, born in West End, New Jersey, be-
came a member of* The New Yorker *magazine group in its
early days. Her short stories, poems and literary criticism
are marked by irony, satire and cynical utterances. (A typical
Dorothy Parker poem may be found on page 214, in the
Poetry section of this book.) At times Miss Parker's sophis-
ticated wit explodes with sharply pointed barbs that are
bitter and angry. However, many of her poems and her prose
pieces reveal a sense of social consciousness and a sympathetic
feeling for unhappy and powerless people.*

THE WALTZ

Why, thank you so much. I'd adore to.

I don't want to dance with him. I don't want to dance
with anybody. And even if I did, it wouldn't be him. He'd be
well down among the last ten. I've seen the way he dances; it
looks like something you do on Saint Walpurgis Night. Just
think, not a quarter of an hour ago, here I was sitting, feeling
so sorry for the poor girl he was dancing with. And now *I'm*
going to be the poor girl. Well. Isn't it a small world?

And a peach of a world, too. A true little corker. Its events are so fascinatingly unpredictable, are not they? Here I was, minding my own business, not doing a stitch of harm to any living soul. And then he comes into my life, all smiles and city manners, to sue me for the favor of one memorable mazurka. Why, he scarcely knows my name, let alone what it stands for. It stands for Despair, Bewilderment, Futility, Degradation, and Premeditated Murder, but little does he wot. I don't wot his name, either; I haven't any idea what it is. Jukes, would be my guess from the look in his eyes. How do you do, Mr. Jukes? And how is that dear little brother of yours, with the two heads?

Ah, now why did he have to come around me, with his low requests? Why can't he let me lead my own life? I ask so little—just to be left alone in my quiet corner of the table, to do my evening brooding over all my sorrows. And he must come, with his bows and his scrapes and his may-I-have-this-ones. And I had to go and tell him that I'd adore to dance with him. I cannot understand why I wasn't struck right down dead. Yes, and being struck dead would look like a day in the country, compared to struggling out a dance with this boy. But what could I do? Everyone else at the table had got up to dance, except him and me. There was I, trapped. Trapped like a trap in a trap.

What can you say, when a man asks you to dance with him? I most certainly will *not* dance with you, I'll see you in hell first. Why, thank you, I'd like to awfully, but I'm having labor pains. Oh, yes, *do* let's dance together—it's so nice to meet a man who isn't a scaredycat about catching my beri-beri. No. There was nothing for me to do, but say I'd adore to. Well, we might as well get it over with. All right, Cannonball, let's run out on the field. You won the toss; you can lead.

Why, I think it's more of a waltz, really. Isn't it?
We might just listen to the music a second. Shall we? Oh, yes,
it's a waltz. Mind? Why, I'm simply thrilled. I'd love to waltz
with you.

I'd love to waltz with you. I'd love to waltz with you.
I'd love to have my tonsils out, I'd love to be in a midnight
fire at sea. Well, it's too late now. We're getting under way.
Oh. Oh, dear. Oh, dear, dear, dear. Oh, this is even worse
than I thought it would be. I suppose that's the one depend-
able law of life—everything is always worse than you thought
it was going to be. Oh, if I had any real grasp of what this
dance would be like, I'd have held out for sitting it out. Well,
it will probably amount to the same thing in the end. We'll be
sitting it out on the floor in a minute, if he keeps this up.

I'm so glad I brought it to his attention that this is a
waltz they're playing. Heaven knows what might have happened, if he had thought it was something fast; we'd have
blown the sides right out of the building. Why does he
always want to be somewhere that he isn't? Why can't we
stay in one place just long enough to get acclimated? It's this
constant rush, rush, rush, that's the curse of American life.
That's the reason that we're all of us so—*Ow!* For God's sake,
don't *kick*, you idiot; this is only second down. Oh, my shin.
My poor, poor shin, that I've had since I was a little girl!

Oh, no, no, no. Goodness, no. It didn't hurt the least
little bit. And anyway it was my fault. Really it was. Truly.
Well, you're just being sweet, to say that. It really was all my
fault.

I wonder what I'd better do—kill him this instant,
with my naked hands, or wait and let him drop in his traces.
Maybe it's best not to make a scene. I guess I'll just lie low,
and watch the pace get him. He can't keep this up indefinitely

—he's only flesh and blood. Die he must, and die he shall, for what he did to me. I don't want to be of the over-sensitive type, but you can't tell me that kick was unpremeditated. Freud says there are no accidents. I've led no cloistered life, I've known dancing partners who have spoiled my slippers and torn my dress; but when it comes to kicking, I am Out-raged Womanhood. When you kick me in the shin, *smile*.

Maybe he didn't do it maliciously. Maybe it's just his way of showing his high spirits. I suppose I ought to be glad that one of us is having such a good time. I suppose I ought to think myself lucky if he brings me back alive. Maybe it's captious to demand of a practically strange man that he leave your shins as he found them. After all, the poor boy's doing the best he can. Probably he grew up in the hill country, and never had no larnin'. I bet they had to throw him on his back to get shoes on him.

Yes, it's lovely, isn't it? It's simply lovely. It's the loveliest waltz. Isn't it? Oh, I think it's lovely, too.

Why, I'm getting positively drawn to the Triple Threat here. He's my hero. He has the heart of a lion, and the sinews of a buffalo. Look at him—never a thought of the consequences, never afraid of his face, hurling himself into every scrimmage, eyes shining, cheeks ablaze. And shall it be said that I hung back? No, a thousand times no. What's it to me if I have to spend the next couple of years in a plaster cast? Come on, Butch, right through them! Who wants to live forever?

Oh. Oh, dear. Oh, he's all right, thank goodness. For a while I thought they'd have to carry him off the field. Ah, I couldn't bear to have anything happen to him. I love him. I love him better than anybody in the world. Look at the spirit he gets into a dreary, commonplace waltz; how effete the other dancers seem, beside him. He is youth and vigor and courage, he is strength and gaiety and—*Ow!* Get off my instep, you hulking peasant! What do you think I am, anyway —a gangplank? *Ow!*

No, of course it didn't hurt. Why, it didn't a bit. Honestly. And it was all my fault. You see, that little step of yours—well, it's perfectly lovely, but it's just a tiny bit tricky to follow at first. Oh, did you work it up yourself? You really did? Well, aren't you amazing! Oh, now I think I've got it. Oh, I think it's lovely. I was watching you do it when you were dancing before. It's awfully effective when you look at it.

It's awfully effective when you look at it. I bet I'm awfully effective when you look at me. My hair is hanging along my cheeks, my skirt is swaddling about me, I can feel the cold damp of my brow. I must look like something out of the "Fall of the House of Usher." This sort of thing takes a fearful toll of a woman my age. And he worked up his little step himself, he with his degenerate cunning. And it was just a tiny bit tricky at first, but now I think I've got it. Two stumbles, slip and a twenty-yard dash; yes. I've got it. I've got several other things too, including a split shin and a bitter heart. I hate this creature I'm chained to. I hated him the moment I saw his leering, bestial face. And here I've been locked in his noxious embrace for the thirty-five years this waltz has lasted. Is that orchestra never going to stop playing? Or must this obscene travesty of a dance go on until hell burns out?

Oh, they're going to play another encore. Oh, goody. Oh, that's lovely. Tired? I should say I'm not tired. I'd like to go on like this forever.

I should say I'm not tired. I'm dead, that's all I am.

Dead, and in what a cause! And the music is never going to stop playing, and we're going on like this, Double-Time Charlie and I, throughout eternity. I suppose I won't care any more, after the first hundred thousand years. I suppose nothing will matter then, not heat nor pain nor broken heart nor cruel, aching weariness. Well. It can't come too soon for me.

I wonder why I didn't tell him I was tired. I wonder why I didn't suggest going back to the table. I could have said let's just listen to the music. Yes, and if he would, that would be the first bit of attention he has given it all evening. George Jean Nathan said that the lovely rhythms of the waltz should be listened to in stillness and not be accompanied by strange gyrations of the human body. I think that's what he said. I think it was George Jean Nathan. Anyhow, whatever he said and whoever he was and whatever he's doing now, he's better off than I am. That's safe. Anybody who isn't waltzing with this Mrs. O'Leary's cow I've got here is having a good time.

Still if we were back at the table, I'd probably have to talk to him. Look at him—what could you say to a thing like that! Did you go to the circus this year, what's your favorite kind of ice cream, how do you spell cat? I guess I'm as well off here. As well off as if I were in a cement mixer in full action.

I'm past all feeling now. The only way I can tell when he steps on me is that I can hear the splintering of bones. And all the events of my life are passing before my eyes. There was the time I was in a hurricane in the West Indies, there was the day I got my head cut open in the taxi smash, there was the night the drunken lady threw a bronze ash-tray at her own true love and got me instead, there was that summer that the sailboat kept capsizing. Ah, what an easy, peaceful time was mine, until I fell in with Swifty, here. I didn't know what trouble was, before I got drawn into this *danse macabre*. I think my mind is beginning to wander. It almost seems to me as if the orchestra were stopping. It couldn't be, of course; it could never, never be. And yet in my ears there is a silence like the sound of angel voices. . . .

Oh, they've stopped, the mean things. They're not going to play any more. Oh, darn. Oh, do you think they would? Do you really think so, if you gave them twenty dollars? Oh, that would be lovely. And look, do tell them to play this same thing. I'd simply adore to go on waltzing.

F. Scott Fitzgerald (1896–1940)

The stories of F. Scott Fitzgerald were social chronicles, describing the restlessness of his generation, and the confusion and tragic nature of life in the twenties. Acclaimed as the social historian and prophet of the Jazz Age, a term he coined, Fitzgerald wrote about the revolt of youth and their eventual disenchantment. Constantly he expressed his sadness and disappointment in American life.

The heroes in Fitzgerald's short stories and novels are middle-class young men who try to understand the world and to remake it in their own image, but each one is inevitably defeated. The tragic flaw in many of these men is their irresponsibility and carelessness. Fitzgerald is a first-rate storyteller who knows how to create an interesting narrative with live characters. Born in St. Paul, Minnesota, F. Scott Fitzgerald attended Princeton.

WINTER DREAMS

Some of the caddies were poor as sin and lived in one-room houses with a neurasthenic cow in the front yard, but Dexter Green's father owned the second best grocery store in Black Bear—the best one was "The Hub," patronized by the wealthy people from Sherry Island—and Dexter caddied only for pocket money.

In the fall when the days became crisp and gray, and the long Minnesota winter shut down like the white lid of a box, Dexter's skis moved over the snow that hid the fairways of the golf course. At these times the country gave him a feeling of profound melancholy—it offended him that the links should lie in enforced fallowness, haunted by ragged sparrows for the long season. It was dreary, too, that on tees where the gay colors fluttered in summer there were now only the desolate sandboxes knee-deep in crusted ice. When he crossed the hills the wind blew cold as misery, and if the sun was out he tramped with his eyes squinted up against the hard dimensionless glare.

In April the winter ceased abruptly. The snow ran down into Black Bear Lake scarcely tarrying for the early golfers to brave the season with red and black balls. Without elation, without an interval of moist glory, the cold was gone.

Dexter knew that there was something dismal about this Northern spring, just as he knew there was something gorgeous about the fall. Fall made him clinch his hands and tremble and repeat idiotic sentences to himself, and make brisk abrupt gestures of command to imaginary audiences and armies. October filled him with hope which November raised to a sort of ecstatic triumph, and in this mood the fleeting brilliant impressions of the summer at Sherry Island were ready grist to his mill. He became a golf champion and defeated Mr. T. A. Hedrick in a marvellous match played a hundred times over the fairways of his imagination, a match each detail of which he changed about untiringly—sometimes he won with almost laughable ease, sometimes he came up magnificently from behind. Again, stepping from a Pierce-Arrow automobile, like Mr. Mortimer Jones, he strolled frigidly into the lounge of the Sherry Island Golf Club—or perhaps, surrounded by an admiring crowd, he gave an exhibition of fancy diving from the springboard of the club raft . . . Among those who watched him in open-mouthed wonder was Mr. Mortimer Jones.

And one day it came to pass that Mr. Jones—himself and not his ghost—came up to Dexter with tears in his eyes and said that Dexter was the ——— best caddy in the club, and wouldn't he decide not to quit if Mr. Jones made it worth his while, because every other ——— caddy in the club lost one ball a hole for him—regularly——

"No, sir," said Dexter decisively, "I don't want to caddy any more." Then, after a pause: "I'm too old."

"You're not more than fourteen. Why the devil did you decide just this morning that you wanted to quit? You promised that next week you'd go over to the state tournament with me."

"I decided I was too old."

Dexter handed in his "A Class" badge, collected what money was due him from the caddy master, and walked home to Black Bear Village.

"The best ——— caddy I ever saw," shouted Mr. Mortimer Jones over a drink that afternoon. "Never lost a ball! Willing! Intelligent! Quiet! Honest! Grateful!"

The little girl who had done this was eleven—beautifully ugly as little girls are apt to be who are destined after a few years to be inexpressibly lovely and bring no end of misery to a great number of men. The spark, however, was perceptible. There was a general ungodliness in the way her lips twisted down at the corners when she smiled, and in the—Heaven help us!—in the almost passionate quality of her eyes. Vitality is born early in such women. It was utterly in evidence now, shining through her thin frame in a sort of glow.

She had come eagerly out on to the course at nine o'clock with a white linen nurse and five small new golf-clubs in a white canvas bag which the nurse was carrying. When Dexter first saw her she was standing by the caddy house, rather ill at ease and trying to conceal the fact by engaging her nurse in an obviously unnatural conversation graced by startling and irrelevant grimaces from herself.

"Well, it's certainly a nice day, Hilda," Dexter heard her say. She drew down the corners of her mouth, smiled, and glanced furtively around, her eyes in transit falling for an instant on Dexter.

Then to the nurse:

"Well, I guess there aren't very many people out here this morning, are there?"

The smile again—radiant, blatantly artificial—convincing.

"I don't know what we're suposed to do now," said the nurse, looking nowhere in particular.

"Oh, that's all right. I'll fix it up."

Dexter stood perfectly still, his mouth slightly ajar. He knew that if he moved forward a step his stare would be in her line of vision—if he moved backward he would lose his full view of her face. For a moment he had not realized how young she was. Now he remembered having seen her several times the year before—in bloomers.

Suddenly, involuntarily, he laughed, a short abrupt laugh—then, startled by himself, he turned and began to walk quickly away.

"Boy!"

Dexter stopped.

"Boy——"

Beyond question he was addressed. Not only that, but he was treated to that absurd smile, that preposterous smile—the memory of which at least a dozen men were to carry into middle age.

"Boy, do you know where the golf teacher is?"

"He's giving a lesson."

"Well, do you know where the caddy master is?"

"He isn't here yet this morning."

"Oh." For a moment this baffled her. She stood alternately on her right and left foot.

"We'd like to get a caddy," said the nurse. "Mrs. Mortimer Jones sent us out to play golf, and we don't know how without we get a caddy."

Here she was stopped by an ominous glance from Miss Jones, followed immediately by the smile.

"There aren't any caddies here except me," said Dexter to the nurse, "and I got to stay here in charge until the caddy master gets here."

"Oh."

Miss Jones and her retinue now withdrew, and at a proper distance from Dexter became involved in a heated conversation, which was concluded by Miss Jones taking one of the clubs and hitting it on the ground with violence. For further emphasis she raised it again and was about to bring it down smartly upon the nurse's bosom, when the nurse seized the club and twisted it from her hands.

"You damn little mean old *thing!*" cried Miss Jones wildly.

Another argument ensued. Realizing that the elements of comedy were implied in the scene, Dexter several times began to laugh, but each time restrained the laugh before it reached audibility. He could not resist the monstrous conviction that the little girl was justified in beating the nurse.

The situation was resolved by the fortuitous appearance of the caddy master, who was appealed to immediately by the nurse.

"Miss Jones is to have a little caddy, and this one says he can't go."

"Mr. McKenna said I was to wait here till you came," said Dexter quickly.

"Well, he's here now." Miss Jones smiled cheerfully at the caddy master. Then she dropped her bag and set off at a haughty mince toward the first tee.

"Well?" The caddy master turned to Dexter. "What you standing there like a dummy for? Go pick up the young lady's clubs."

"I don't think I'll go out today," said Dexter.

"You don't——"

"I think I'll quit."

The enormity of his decision frightened him. He was a favorite caddy, and the thirty dollars a month he earned through the summer were not to be made elsewhere around the lake. But he had received a strong emotional shock, and his perturbation required a violent and immediate outlet.

It is not so simple as that, either. As so frequently would be the case in the future, Dexter was unconsciously dictated to by his winter dreams.

II

Now, of course, the quality and the seasonability of these winter dreams varied, but the stuff of them remained. They persuaded Dexter several years later to pass up a busi-

ness course at the State university—his father, prospering
now, would have paid his way—for the precarious advantage
of attending an older and more famous university in the
East, where he was bothered by his scanty funds. But do
not get the impression, because his winter dreams happened
to be concerned at first with musings on the rich, that there
was anything merely snobbish in the boy. He wanted not
association with glittering things and glittering people—he
wanted the glittering things themselves. Often he reached
out for the best without knowing why he wanted it—and
sometimes he ran up against the mysterious denials and
prohibitions in which life indulges. It is with one of those
denials and not with his career as a whole that this story deals.

He made money. It was rather amazing. After college
he went to the city from which Black Bear Lake draws its
wealthy patrons. When he was only twenty-three and had
been there not quite two years, there were already people
who liked to say: "Now *there's* a boy—." All about him rich
men's sons were peddling bonds precariously, or investing
patrimonies precariously, or plodding through the two dozen
volumes of the "George Washington Commercial Course,"
but Dexter borrowed a thousand dollars on his college degree
and his confident mouth, and bought a partnership in a
laundry.

It was a small laundry when he went into it, but
Dexter made a specialty of learning how the English washed
fine woolen golf stockings without shrinking them, and
within a year he was catering to the trade that wore knicker-
bockers. Men were insisting that their Shetland hose and
sweaters go to his laundry, just as they had insisted on a
caddy who could find golf balls. A little later he was doing
their wives' lingerie as well—and running five branches in

different parts of the city. Before he was twenty-seven he owned the largest string of laundries in his section of the country. It was then that he sold out and went to New York. But the part of his story that concerns us goes back to the days when he was making his first big success.

When he was twenty-three Mr. Hart—one of the gray-haired men who liked to say "Now there's a boy—" gave him a guest card to the Sherry Island Golf Club for a weekend. So he signed his name one day on the register, and that afternoon played golf in a foursome with Mr. Hart and Mr. Sandwood and Mr. T. A. Hedrick. He did not consider it necessary to remark that he had once carried Mr. Hart's bag over this same links, and that he knew every trap and gully with his eyes shut—but he found himself glancing at the four caddies who trailed them, trying to catch a gleam or gesture that would remind him of himself, that would lessen the gap which lay between his present and his past.

It was a curious day, slashed abruptly with fleeting, familiar impressions. One minute he had the sense of being a trespasser—in the next he was impressed by the tremendous superiority he felt toward Mr. T. A. Hedrick, who was a bore and not even a good golfer any more.

Then, because of a ball Mr. Hart lost near the fifteenth green, an enormous thing happened. While they were searching the stiff grasses of the rough there was a clear call of "Fore!" from behind a hill in their rear. And as they all turned abruptly from their search a bright new ball sliced abruptly over the hill and caught Mr. T. A. Hedrick in the abdomen.

"By Gad!" cried Mr. T. A. Hedrick, "they ought to put some of these crazy women off the course, It's getting to be outrageous."

A head and a voice came up to together over the hill:
"Do you mind if we go through?"

"You hit me in the stomach!" declared Mr. Hedrick
wildly.

"Did I?" The girl approached the group of men. "I'm
sorry. I yelled 'Fore!'"

Her glance fell casually on each of the men—then
scanned the fairway for her ball.

"Did I bounce into the rough?"

It was impossible to determine whether this question
was ingenuous or malicious. In a moment, however, she left
no doubt, for as her partner came up over the hill she
called cheerfully:

"Here I am! I'd have gone on the green except that
I hit something."

As she took her stance for a short mashie shot, Dexter
looked at her closely. She wore a blue gingham dress, rimmed
at throat and shoulders with a white edging that accentuated
her tan. The quality of exaggeration, of thinness, which had
made her passionate eyes and down-turning mouth absurd
at eleven, was gone now. She was arrestingly beautiful. The
color in her cheeks was centred like the color in a picture
—it was not a "high" color, but a sort of fluctuating and
feverish warmth, so shaded that it seemed at any moment
it would recede and disappear. This color and the mobility
of her mouth gave a continual impression of flux, of intense
life, of passionate vitality—balanced only partially by the
sad luxury of her eyes.

She swung her mashie impatiently and without interest, pitching the ball into a sand pit on the other side of
the green. With a quick, insincere smile and a careless "Thank
you!" she went on after it.

"That Judy Jones!" remarked Mr. Hedrick on the next tee, as they waited—some moments—for her to play on ahead. "All she needs is to be turned up and spanked for six months and then to be married off to an old-fashioned cavalry captain."

"My God, she's good-looking!" said Mr. Sandwood, who was just over thirty.

"Good-looking!" cried Mr. Hedrick contemptuously, "she always looks as if she wanted to be kissed! Turning those big cow eyes on every calf in town!"

It was doubtful if Mr. Hedrick intended a reference to the maternal instinct.

"She'd play pretty good golf if she'd try," said Mr. Sandwood.

"She has no form," said Mr. Hedrick solemnly.

"She has a nice figure," said Mr. Sandwood.

"Better thank the Lord she doesn't drive a swifter ball," said Mr. Hart, winking at Dexter.

Later in the afternoon the sun went down with a riotous swirl of gold and varying blues and scarlets, and left the dry, rustling night of Western summer. Dexter watched from the veranda of the Golf Club, watched the even overlap of the waters in the little wind, silver molasses under the harvest moon. Then the moon held a finger to her lips and the lake became a clear pool, pale and quiet. Dexter put on his bathing suit and swam out to the farthest raft, where he stretched dripping on the wet canvas of the springboard.

There was a fish jumping and a star shining and the lights around the lake were gleaming. Over on a dark peninsula a piano was playing the songs of last summer and of summers before that—songs from "Chin-Chin" and "The Count of Luxemburg" and "The Chocolate Soldier"—and because the sound of a piano over a stretch of water had always seemed beautiful to Dexter he lay perfectly quiet and listened.

The tune the piano was playing at that moment had been gay and new five years before when Dexter was a sophomore at college. They had played it at a prom once when he could not afford the luxury of proms, and he had stood outside the gymnasium and listened. The sound of the tune precipitated in him a sort of ecstasy and it was with that ecstasy he viewed what happened to him now. It was a mood of intense appreciation, a sense that, for once, he was magnificently attune to life and that everything about him was radiating a brightness and a glamour he might never know again.

A low, pale oblong detached itself suddenly from the darkness of the Island, spitting forth the reverberate sound of a racing motorboat. Two white streamers of cleft water rolled themselves out behind it and almost immediately the boat was beside him, drowning out the hot tinkle of the piano in the drone of its spray. Dexter raising himself on his arms was aware of a figure standing at the wheel, of two dark eyes regarding him over the lengthening space of water —then the boat had gone by and was sweeping in an immense and purposeless circle of spray round and round in the middle of the lake. With equal eccentricity one of the circles flattened out and headed back toward the raft.

"Who's that?" she called, shutting off her motor. She was so near now that Dexter could see her bathing suit, which consisted apparently of pink rompers.

The nose of the boat bumped the raft, and as the latter tilted rakishly he was precipitated toward her. With different degrees of interest they recognized each other.

"Aren't you one of those men we played through this afternoon?" she demanded.

He was.

"Well, do you know how to drive a motorboat? Because if you do I wish you'd drive this one so I can ride on the surfboard behind. My name is Judy Jones"—she favored him with an absurd smirk—rather, what tried to be a smirk, for, twist her mouth as she might, it was not grotesque, it was merely beautiful—"and I live in a house over there on the Island, and in that house there is a man waiting for me. When he drove up at the door I drove out of the dock because he says I'm his ideal."

There was a fish jumping and a star shining and the lights around the lake were gleaming. Dexter sat beside Judy Jones and she explained how her boat was driven. Then she was in the water, swimming to the floating surfboard with a sinuous crawl. Watching her was without effort to the eyes, watching a branch waving or a seagull flying. Her arms, burned to butternut, moved sinuously among the dull platinum ripples, elbow appearing first, casting the forearm back with a cadence of falling water, then reaching out and down, stabbing a path ahead.

They moved out into the lake; turning, Dexter saw that she was kneeling on the low rear of the now uptilted surfboard.

"Go faster," she called, "fast as it'll go."

Obediently he jammed the lever forward and the white spray mounted at the bow. When he looked around again the girl was standing up on the rushing board, her arms spread wide, her eyes lifted toward the moon.

"It's awful cold," she shouted. "What's your name?"

He told her.

"Well, why don't you come to dinner tomorrow night?"

His heart turned over like the flywheel of the boat, and, for the second time, her casual whim gave a new direction to his life.

III

Next evening while he waited for her to come downstairs, Dexter peopled the soft deep summer room and the sun porch that opened from it with the men who had already loved Judy Jones. He knew the sort of men they were—the men who when he first went to college had entered from the great prep schools with graceful clothes and the deep tan of healthy summers. He had seen that, in one sense, he was better than these men. He was newer and stronger. Yet in acknowledging to himself that he wished his children to be like them he was admitting that he was but the rough, strong stuff from which they eternally sprang.

When the time had come for him to wear good clothes, he had known who were the best tailors in America, and the best tailors in America had made him the suit he wore this evening. He had acquired that particular reserve peculiar to his university, that set it off from other universities. He recognized the value to him of such a mannerism and he had adopted it; he knew that to be careless in dress and manner required more confidence than to be careful. But carelessness was for his children. His mother's name had been Krimslich. She was a Bohemian of the peasant class and she had talked broken English to the end of her days. Her son must keep to the set patterns.

At a little after seven Judy Jones came downstairs.

She wore a blue silk afternoon dress, and he was disappointed at first that she had not put on something more elaborate. This feeling was accentuated when, after a brief greeting, she went to the door of a butler's pantry and pushing it open called: "You can serve dinner, Martha." He had rather expected that a butler would announce dinner, that there would be a cocktail. Then he put these thoughts behind him as they sat down side by side on a lounge and looked at each other.

"Father and mother won't be here," she said thoughtfully.

He remembered the last time he had seen her father, and he was glad the parents were not to be here tonight— they might wonder who he was. He had been born in Keeble, a Minnesota village fifty miles farther north, and he always gave Keeble as his home instead of Black Bear Village. Country towns were well enough to come from if they weren't inconveniently in sight and used as footstools by fashionable lakes.

They talked of his university, which she had visited frequently during the past two years, and of the near-by city which supplied Sherry Island with its patrons, and whither Dexter would return next day to his prospering laundries.

During dinner she slipped into a moody depression which gave Dexter a feeling of uneasiness. Whatever petulance she uttered in her throaty voice worried him. Whatever she smiled at—at him, at a chicken liver, at nothing—it disturbed him that her smile could have no root in mirth, or even in amusement. When the scarlet corners of her lips curved down, it was less a smile than an invitation to a kiss.

Then, after dinner, she led him out on the dark sun-porch and deliberately changed the atmosphere.

"Do you mind if I weep a little?" she said.

"I'm afraid I'm boring you," he responded quickly.

"You're not. I like you. But I've just had a terrible afternoon. There was a man I cared about, and this afternoon he told me out of a clear sky that he was poor as a church mouse. He'd never even hinted it before. Does this sound horribly mundane?"

"Perhaps he was afraid to tell you."

"Suppose he was," she answered. "He didn't start right. You see, if I'd thought of him as poor—well, I've been mad about loads of poor men, and fully intended to marry them all. But in this case, I hadn't thought of him that way, and my interest in him wasn't strong enough to survive the shock. As if a girl calmly informed her fiancé that she was a widow. He might not object to widows, but——

"Let's start right," she interrupted herself suddenly. "Who are you, anyhow?"

For a moment Dexter hesitated. Then:

"I'm nobody," he announced. "My career is largely a matter of futures."

"Are you poor?"

"No," he said frankly. "I'm probably making more money than any man my age in the Northwest. I know that's an obnoxious remark, but you advised me to start right."

There was a pause. Then she smiled and the corners of her mouth drooped and an almost imperceptible sway brought her closer to him, looking up into his eyes. A lump rose in Dexter's throat, and he waited breathless for the experiment, facing the unpredictable compound that would form mysteriously from the elements of their lips. Then he saw—she communicated her excitement to him, lavishly, deeply, with kisses that were not a promise but a fulfilment. They aroused in him not hunger demanding renewal but surfeit that would demand more surfeit . . . kisses that were like charity, creating want by holding back nothing at all.

It did not take him many hours to decide that he had wanted Judy Jones ever since he was a proud, desirous little boy.

IV

It began like that—and continued, with varying shades of intensity, on such a note right up to the dénouement. Dexter surrendered a part of himself to the most direct and unprincipled personality with which he had ever come in contact. Whatever Judy wanted, she went after with the full pressure of her charm. There was no divergence of method, no jockeying for position or premeditation of effects —there was a very little mental side to any of her affairs. She simply made men conscious to the highest degree of her physical loveliness. Dexter had no desire to change her. Her deficiencies were knit up with a passionate energy that transcended and justified them.

When, as Judy's head lay against his shoulder that first night, she whispered, "I don't know what's the matter with me. Last night I thought I was in love with a man and tonight I think I'm in love with you——"—it seemed to him a beautiful and romantic thing to say. It was the exquisite excitability that for the moment he controlled and owned. But a week later he was compelled to view this same quality in a different light. She took him in her roadster to a picnic supper, and after supper she disappeared, likewise in her roadster, with another man. Dexter became enormously upset and was scarcely able to be decently civil to the other people present. When she assured him that she had not kissed the other man, he knew she was lying—yet he was glad that she had taken the trouble to lie to him.

He was, as he found before the summer ended, one of a varying dozen who circulated about her. Each of them had at one time been favored above all others—about half of them still basked in the solace of occasional sentimental revivals. Whenever one showed signs of dropping out through long neglect, she granted him a brief honeyed hour, which encouraged him to tag along for a year or so longer. Judy made these forays upon the helpless and defeated without malice, indeed half unconscious that there was anything mischievous in what she did.

When a new man came to town every one dropped out—dates were automatically cancelled.

The helpless part of trying to do anything about it was that she did it all herself. She was not a girl who could be "won" in the kinetic sense—she was proof against cleverness, she was proof against charm; if any of these assailed her too strongly she would immediately resolve the affair to a physical basis, and under the magic of her physical splendor the strong as well as the brilliant played her game and not their own. She was entertained only by the gratification of her desires and by the direct exercise of her own charm. Perhaps from so much youthful love, so many youthful lovers, she had come, in self-defense, to nourish herself wholly from within.

Succeeding Dexter's first exhilaration came restlessness and dissatisfaction. The helpless ecstasy of losing himself in her was opiate rather than tonic. It was fortunate for his work during the winter that those moments of ecstasy came infrequently. Early in their acquaintance it had seemed for a while that there was a deep and spontaneous mutual attraction—that first August, for example—three days of long evenings on her dusky veranda, of strange wan kisses through the late afternoon, in shadowy alcoves or behind the protecting trellises of the garden arbors, of mornings when she was fresh as a dream and almost shy at meeting him in the clarity of the rising day. There was all the ecstasy of an engagement about it, sharpened by his realization that there was no engagement. It was during those three days that, for the first time, he had asked her to marry him. She said "maybe some day," she said "kiss me," she said "I'd like to marry you," she said "I love you"—she said—nothing.

The three days were interrupted by the arrival of a New York man who visited at her house for half September. To Dexter's agony, rumor engaged them. The man was the son of the president of a great trust company. But at the end of a month it was reported that Judy was yawning. At a dance one night she sat all evening in a motorboat with a local beau, while the New Yorker searched the club for her frantically. She told the local beau that she was bored with her visitor, and two days later he left. She was seen with him at the station, and it was reported that he looked very mournful indeed.

On this note the summer ended. Dexter was twenty-four, and he found himself increasingly in a position to do as he wished. He joined two clubs in the city and lived at one of them. Though he was by no means an integral part of the stag lines at these clubs, he managed to be on hand at dances where Judy Jones was likely to appear. He could have gone out socially as much as he liked—he was an eligible young man, now, and popular with downtown fathers. His confessed devotion to Judy Jones had rather solidified his position. But he had no social aspirations and rather despised the dancing men who were always on tap for the Thursday or Saturday parties and who filled in at dinners with the younger married set. Already he was playing with the idea of going East to New York. He wanted to take Judy Jones with him. No disillusion as to the world in which she had grown up could cure his illusion as to her desirability.

Remember that—for only in the light of it can what he did for her be understood.

Eighteen months after he first met Judy Jones he became engaged to another girl. Her name was Irene Scheerer, and her father was one of the men who had always believed in Dexter. Irene was light-haired and sweet and honorable, and a little stout, and she had two suitors whom she pleasantly relinquished when Dexter formally asked her to marry him.

Summer, fall, winter, spring, another summer, another fall—so much he had given of his active life to the incorrigible lips of Judy Jones. She had treated him with interest, with encouragement, with malice, with indifference, with contempt. She had inflicted on him the innumerable little slights and indignities possible in such a case—as if in revenge for having ever cared for him at all. She had beckoned him and yawned at him and beckoned him again and he had responded often with bitterness and narrowed eyes. She had brought him ecstatic happiness and intolerable agony of spirit. She had caused him untold inconvenience and not a little trouble. She had insulted him, and she had ridden over him, and she had played his interest in her against his interest in his work—for fun. She had done everything to him except to criticise him—this she had not done—it seemed to him only because it might have sullied the utter indifference she manifested and sincerely felt toward him.

When autumn had come and gone again it occurred to him that he could not have Judy Jones. He had to beat this into his mind but he convinced himself at last. He lay awake at night for a while and argued it over. He told himself the trouble and the pain she had caused him, he enumerated her glaring deficiencies as a wife. Then he said to himself that he loved her, and after a while he fell asleep. For a week, lest he imagined her husky voice over the telephone or her eyes opposite him at lunch, he worked hard and late, and at night he went to his office and plotted out his years.

At the end of a week he went to a dance and cut in on her once. For almost the first time since they had met he did not ask her to sit out with him or tell her that she was lovely. It hurt him that she did not miss these things—that was all. He was not jealous when he saw that there was a new man tonight. He had been hardened against jealousy long before.

He stayed late at the dance. He sat for an hour with Irene Scheerer and talked about books and about music. He knew very little about either. But he was beginning to be master of his own time now, and he had a rather priggish notion that he—the young and already fabulously successful Dexter Green—should know more about such things.

That was in October, when he was twenty-five. In January, Dexter and Irene became engaged. It was to be announced in June, and they were to be married three months later.

The Minnesota winter prolonged itself interminably,

and it was almost May when the winds came soft and the snow ran down into Black Bear Lake at last. For the first time in over a year Dexter was enjoying a certain tranquillity of spirit. Judy Jones had been in Florida, and afterward in Hot Springs, and somewhere she had been engaged, and somewhere she had broken it off. At first, when Dexter had definitely given her up, it had made him sad that people still linked them together and asked for news of her, but when he began to be placed at dinner next to Irene Scheerer people didn't ask him about her any more—they told him about her. He ceased to be an authority on her.

May at last. Dexter walked the streets at night when the darkness was damp as rain, wondering that so soon, with so little done, so much of ecstasy had gone from him. May one year back had been marked by Judy's poignant, unforgivable, yet forgiven turbulence—it had been one of those rare times when he fancied she had grown to care for him. That old penny's worth of happiness he had spent for this bushel of content. He knew that Irene would be no more than a curtain spread behind him, a hand moving among gleaming teacups, a voice calling to children . . . fire and loveliness were gone, the magic of nights and the wonder of the varying hours and seasons . . . slender lips, down-turning, dropping to his lips and bearing him up into a heaven of eyes. . . . The thing was deep in him. He was too strong and alive for it to die lightly.

In the middle of May when the weather balanced for a few days on the thin bridge that led to deep summer he turned in one night at Irene's house. Their engagement was to be announced in a week now—no one would be surprised at it. And tonight they would sit together on the lounge at the University Club and look on for an hour at the dancers. It gave him a sense of solidity to go with her—she was so sturdily popular, so intensely "great."

He mounted the steps of the brownstone house and stepped inside.

"Irene," he called.

Mrs. Scheerer came out of the living room to meet him.

"Dexter," she said, "Irene's gone upstairs with a splitting headache. She wanted to go with you but I made her go to bed."

"Nothing serious, I——"

"Oh, no. She's going to play golf with you in the morning. You can spare her for just one night, can't you, Dexter?"

Her smile was kind. She and Dexter liked each other. In the living room he talked for a moment before he said good night.

Returning to the University Club, where he had rooms, he stood in the doorway for a moment and watched the dancers. He leaned against the doorpost, nodded at a man or two—yawned.

"Hello darling."

The familiar voice at his elbow startled him. Judy Jones had left a man and crossed the room to him—Judy Jones, a slender enamelled doll in cloth of gold: gold in a band at her head, gold in two slipper points at her dress's hem. The fragile glow of her face seemed to blossom as she smiled at him. A breeze of warmth and light blew through the room. His hands in the pockets of his dinner jacket tightened spasmodically. He was filled with a sudden excitement.

"When did you get back?" he asked casually.

"Come here and I'll tell you about it."

She turned and he followed her. She had been away —he could have wept at the wonder of her return. She had passed through enchanted streets, doing things that were like provocative music. All mysterious happenings, all fresh and quickening hopes, had gone away with her, come back with her now.

She turned in the doorway.

"Have you a car here? If you haven't, I have."

"I have a coupé."

In then, with a rustle of golden cloth. He slammed the door. Into so many cars she had stepped—like this— like that—her back against the leather, so—her elbow resting on the door—waiting. She would have been soiled long since had there been anything to soil her—except herself—but this was her own self outpouring.

With an effort he forced himself to start the car and back into the street. This was nothing, he must remember. She had done this before, and he had put her behind him, as he would have crossed a bad account from his books.

He drove slowly downtown and, affecting abstraction, traversed the deserted streets of the business section, peopled here and there where a movie was giving out its crowd or where consumptive or pugilistic youth lounged in front of pool halls. The clink of glasses and the slap of hands on the bars issued from saloons, cloisters of glazed glass and dirty yellow light.

She was watching him closely and the silence was embarrassing, yet in this crisis he could find no casual word with which to profane the hour. At a convenient turning he began to zigzag back toward the University Club.

"Have you missed me?" she asked suddenly.

"Everybody missed you."

He wondered if she knew of Irene Scheerer. She had been back only a day—her absence had been almost contemporaneous with his engagement.

"What a remark!" Judy laughed sadly—without sadness. She looked at him searchingly. He became absorbed in the dashboard.

"You're handsomer than you used to be," she said thoughtfully. "Dexter, you have the most rememberable eyes."

He could have laughed at this, but he did not laugh. It was the sort of thing that was said to sophomores. Yet it stabbed at him.

"I'm awfully tired of everything, darling." She called every one darling, endowing the endearment with careless, individual camaraderie. "I wish you'd marry me."

The directness of this confused him. He should have told her now that he was going to marry another girl, but he could not tell her. He could as easily have sworn that he had never loved her.

"I think we'd get along," she continued, on the same note, "unless probably you've forgotten me and fallen in love with another girl."

Her confidence was obviously enormous. She had said, in effect, that she found such a thing impossible to believe, that if it were true he had merely committed a childish indiscretion—and probably to show off. She would forgive him, because it was not a matter of any moment but rather something to be brushed aside lightly.

"Of course you could never love anybody but me," she continued, "I like the way you love me. Oh, Dexter, have you forgotten last year?"

"No, I haven't forgotten."

"Neither have I!"

Was she sincerely moved—or was she carried along by the wave of her own acting?

"I wish we could be like that again," she said, and he forced himself to answer:

"I don't think we can."

"I suppose not. . . . I hear you're giving Irene Scheerer a violent rush."

There was not the faintest emphasis on the name, yet Dexter was suddenly ashamed.

"Oh, take me home," cried Judy suddenly; "I don't want to go back to that idiotic dance—with those children."

Then, as he turned up the street that led to the residence district, Judy began to cry quietly to herself. He had never seen her cry before.

The dark street lightened, the dwellings of the rich loomed up around them, he stopped his coupé in front of the great white bulk of the Mortimer Joneses' house, somnolent, gorgeous, drenched with the splendor of the damp moonlight. Its solidity startled him. The strong walls, the steel of the girders, the breadth and beam and pomp of it were there only to bring out the contrast with the young beauty beside him. It was sturdy to accentuate her slightness—as if to show what a breeze could be generated by a butterfly's wing.

He sat perfectly quiet, his nerves in wild clamor, afraid that if he moved he would find her irresistibly in his arms. Two tears had rolled down her wet face and trembled on her upper lip.

"I'm more beautiful than anybody else," she said brokenly, "why can't I be happy?" Her moist eyes tore at his stability—her mouth turned slowly downward with an exquisite sadness: "I'd like to marry you if you'd have me,

Dexter. I suppose you think I'm not worth having, but I'll be so beautiful for you, Dexter."

A million phrases of anger, pride, passion, hatred, tenderness fought on his lips. Then a perfect wave of emotion washed over him, carrying off with it a sediment of wisdom, of convention, of doubt, of honor. This was his girl who was speaking, his own, his beautiful, his pride.

"Won't you come in?" He heard her draw in her breath sharply.

Waiting.

"All right," his voice was trembling, "I'll come in."

V

It was strange that neither when it was over nor a long time afterward did he regret that night. Looking at it from the perspective of ten years, the fact that Judy's flare for him endured just one month seemed of little importance. Nor did it matter that by his yielding he subjected himself to a deeper agony in the end and gave serious hurt to Irene Scheerer and to Irene's parents, who had befriended him. There was nothing sufficiently pictorial about Irene's grief to stamp itself on his mind.

Dexter was at bottom hard-minded. The attitude of the city on his action was of no importance to him, not because he was going to leave the city, but because any outside attitude on the situation seemed superficial. He was completely indifferent to popular opinion. Nor, when he had seen that it was no use, that he did not possess in himself the power to move fundamentally or to hold Judy Jones, did he bear any malice toward her. He loved her, and he would love her until the day he was too old for loving—but he could not have her. So he tasted the deep pain that is reserved only for the strong, just as he had tasted for a little while the deep happiness.

Even the ultimate falsity of the grounds upon which Judy terminated the engagement that she did not want to "take him away" from Irene—Judy who had wanted nothing else—did not revolt him. He was beyond any revulsion or any amusement.

He went East in February with the intention of selling out his laundries and settling in New York—but the war came to America in March and changed his plans. He returned to the West, handed over the management of the business to his partner, and went into the first officers' training camp in late April. He was one of those young thousands who greeted the war with a certain amount of relief, welcoming the liberation from webs of tangled emotion.

VI

This story is not his biography, remember, although things creep into it which have nothing to do with those dreams he had when he was young. We are almost done with them and with him now. There is only one more incident to be related here, and it happens seven years farther on.

It took place in New York, where he had done well— so well that there were no barriers too high for him. He was thirty-two years old, and, except for one flying trip immediately after the war, he had not been West in seven years. A man named Devlin from Detroit came into his office to see him in a business way, and then and there this incident occurred, and closed out, so to speak, this particular side of his life.

"So you're from the Middle West," said the man Devlin with careless curiosity. "That's funny—I thought men like you were probably born and raised on Wall Street. You know—wife of one of my best friends in Detroit came from your city. I was an usher at the wedding."

Dexter waited with no apprehension of what was coming.

"Judy Simms," said Devlin with no particular interest; "Judy Jones she was once."

"Yes, I knew her." A dull impatience spread over him. He had heard, of course, that she was married—perhaps deliberately he had heard no more.

"Awfully nice girl," brooded Devlin meaninglessly, "I'm sort of sorry for her."

"Why?" Something in Dexter was alert, receptive, at once.

"Oh, Lud Simms has gone to pieces in a way. I don't mean he ill-uses her, but he drinks and runs around—"

"Doesn't she run around?"

"No. Stays at home with her kids."

"Oh."

"She's a little too old for him," said Devlin.

"Too old!" cried Dexter. "Why, man, she's only twenty-seven."

He was possessed with a wild notion of rushing out into the streets and taking a train to Detroit. He rose to his feet spasmodically.

"I guess you're busy," Devlin apologized quickly. "I didn't realize—"

"No, I'm not busy," said Dexter, steadying his voice. "I'm not busy at all. Not busy at all. Did you say she was—twenty-seven? No, I said she was twenty-seven."

"Yes, you did," agreed Devlin dryly.

"Go on, then. Go on."

"What do you mean?"

"About Judy Jones."

Devlin looked at him helplessly.

"Well, that's—I told you all there is to it. He treats her like the devil. Oh, they're not going to get divorced or anything. When he's particularly outrageous she forgives him. In fact, I'm inclined to think she loves him. She was a pretty girl when she first came to Detroit."

A pretty girl! The phrase struck Dexter as ludicrous.

"Isn't she—a pretty girl, any more?"

"Oh, she's all right."

"Look here," said Dexter, sitting down suddenly. "I don't understand. You say she was a 'pretty girl' and now you say she's 'all right.' I don't understand what you mean —Judy Jones wasn't a pretty girl, at all. She was a great beauty. Why, I knew her, I knew her. She was—"

Devlin laughed pleasantly.

"I'm not trying to start a row," he said. "I think Judy's a nice girl and I like her. I can't understand how a man like Lud Simms could fall madly in love with her, but he did." Then he added: "Most of the women like her."

Dexter looked closely at Devlin, thinking wildly that there must be a reason for this, some insensitivity in the man or some private malice.

"Lots of women fade just like *that*," Devlin snapped his fingers. "You must have seen it happen. Perhaps I've forgotten how pretty she was at her wedding. I've seen her so much since then, you see. She has nice eyes."

A sort of dullness settled down upon Dexter. For the first time in his life he felt like getting very drunk. He knew that he was laughing loudly at something Devlin had said, but he did not know what it was or why it was funny. When, in a few minutes, Devlin went he lay down on his lounge and looked out the window at the New York skyline into which the sun was sinking in dull lovely shades of pink and gold.

He had thought that having nothing else to lose he was invulnerable at last—but he knew that he had just lost something more, as surely as if he had married Judy Jones and seen her fade away before his eyes.

The dream was gone. Something had been taken from him. In a sort of panic he pushed the palms of his hands into his eyes and tried to bring up a picture of the waters lapping on Sherry Island and the moonlit veranda, and gingham on the golf links and the dry sun and the gold color of her neck's soft down. And her mouth damp to his kisses and her eyes plaintive with melancholy and her freshness like new linen in the morning. Why, these things were no longer in the world! They had existed and they existed no longer.

For the first time in years the tears were streaming down his face. But they were for himself now. He did not care about mouth and eyes and moving hands. He wanted to care, and he could not care. For he had gone away and he could never go back any more. The gates were closed, the sun was gone down, and there was no beauty but the gray beauty of steel that withstands time. Even the grief he could have borne was left behind in the country of illusion, of youth, of the richness of life, where his winter dreams had flourished.

"Long ago," he said, "long ago, there was something in me, but now that thing is gone. Now that thing is gone, that thing is gone. I cannot cry. I cannot care. That thing will come back no more."

Thomas Wolfe (1900-1938)

The novels and short stories of Thomas Wolfe are largely autobiographical; in them he attempted to deduce a philosophy from personal experience. A "lost modern" seeking to find his identity, searching for meaning with a hunger for fulfillment, Wolfe, through lyrical and evocative prose, expressed his exuberant feelings about his family, about growing up in the South, about youth and America.

Born in Ashville, North Carolina, Wolfe was graduated from the University of North Carolina. After completing graduate work at Harvard, he taught English at New York University. In the next-to-the-last chapter of his first novel, Look Homeward, Angel, *he describes the thoughts and feelings of Eugene Gant, the central figure of the story, when he goes to visit the cemetery after the death and burial of his brother Ben.*

FROM LOOK HOMEWARD, ANGEL

It was October and the leaves were quaking. Dusk was beginning. The sun had gone, the western ranges faded in chill purple mist, but the western sky still burned with ragged bands of orange. It was October.

Eugene walked swiftly along the sinuous paved curves of Rutledge Road. There was a smell of fog and supper in the air: a warm moist blur at windowpanes, and the pungent sizzle of cookery. There were mist-far voices, and a smell of burning leaves, and a warm yellow blur of lights.

He turned into an unpaved road by the big wooden sanitarium. He heard the rich kitchen laughter of the Negroes, the larded sizzle of food, the dry veranda coughing of the lungers.

He walked briskly along the lumpy road, with a dry scuffling of leaves. The air was a chill dusky pearl: above him a few pale stars were out. The town and the house were behind him. There was a singing in the great hill pines.

Two women came down the road and passed him. He saw that they were country women. They were dressed rustily in black, and one of them was weeping. He thought of the men who had been laid in the earth that day, and of all the women who wept. Will they come again? he wondered.

When he came to the gate of the cemetery he found it open. He went in quickly and walked swiftly up the winding road that curved around the crest of the hill. The grasses were dry and sere; a wilted wreath of laurel lay upon a grave. As he approached the family plot, his pulse quickened a little. Some one was moving slowly, deliberately, in among the gravestones. But as he came up he saw that it was Mrs. Pert.

"Good evening, Mrs. Pert," said Eugene.

"Who is it?" she asked, peering murkily. She came to him with her grave unsteady step.

"It's 'Gene," he said.

"Oh, is it Old 'Gene?" she said. "How are you, 'Gene?"

"Pretty well," he said. He stood awkwardly, chilled,

not knowing how to continue. It was getting dark. There were long lonely preludes to winter in the splendid pines, and a whistling of wind in the long grasses. Below them, in the gulch, night had come. There was a Negro settlement there—Stumptown, it was called. The rich voices of Africa wailed up to them their jungle dirge.

But in the distance, away on their level and above, on other hills, they saw the town. Slowly, in twinkling nests, the lights of the town went up, and there were frost-far voices, and music, and the laughter of a girl.

"This is a nice place," said Eugene. "You get a nice view of the town from here."

"Yes," said Mrs. Pert. "And Old Ben's got the nicest place of all. You get a better view right here than anywhere else. I've been here before in the daytime." In a moment she went on. "Old Ben will turn into lovely flowers. Roses, I think."

"No," said Eugene, "dandelions—and big flowers with a lot of thorns on them."

She stood looking about fuzzily for a moment, with the blurred gentle smile on her lips.

"It is getting dark, Mrs. Pert," said Eugene hesitantly. "Are you out here alone?"

"Alone? I've got Old 'Gene and Old Ben here, haven't I?" she said.

"Maybe we'd better go back, Mrs. Pert?" he said. "It's going to turn cold tonight. I'll go with you."

"Fatty can go by herself," she said with dignity. "Don't worry, 'Gene. I'll leave you alone."

"That's all right," said Eugene, confused. "We both came for the same reason, I suppose."

"Yes," said Mrs. Pert. "Who'll be coming here this

time next year, I wonder? Will Old 'Gene come back then?"

"No," said Eugene. "No, Mrs. Pert. I shall never come here again."

"Nor I, 'Gene," she said. "When do you go back to school?"

"Tomorrow," he said.

"Then Fatty will have to say good-bye," she said reproachfully. "I'm going away too."

"Where are you going?" he asked, surprised.

"I'm going to live with my daughter in Tennessee. You didn't know Fatty was a grandmother, did you?" she said, with her soft blurred smile. "I've a little grandson two years old."

"I'm sorry to see you go," Eugene said.

Mrs. Pert was silent a moment, rocking vaguely upon her feet.

"What did they say was wrong with Ben?" she asked.

"He had pneumonia, Mrs. Pert," said Eugene.

"Oh, pneumonia! That's it!" She nodded her head wisely as if satisfied. "My husband's a drug salesman, you know, but I never can remember all the things that people have. Pneumonia."

She was silent again, reflecting.

"And when they shut you up in a box and put you in the ground, the way they did Old Ben, what do they call that?" she asked with a soft inquiring smile.

He did not laugh.

"They call that death, Mrs. Pert."

"Death! Yes, that's it," said Mrs. Pert brightly, nodding her head in agreement. "That's one kind, 'Gene. There are some other kinds, too. Did you know that?" She smiled at him.

"Yes," said Eugene. "I know that, Mrs. Pert."

She stretched out her hands suddenly to him, and clasped his cold fingers. She did not smile any more.

"Good-bye, my dear," she said. "We both knew Ben, didn't we? God bless you."

Then she turned and walked away down the road, at her portly uncertain gait, and was lost in the gathering dark.

The great stars rode proudly up into heaven. And just over him, just over the town, it seemed, there was one so rich and low he could have touched it. Ben's grave had been that day freshly sodded: there was a sharp cold smell of earth there. Eugene thought of Spring, and the poignant and wordless odor of the elvish dandelions that would be there. In the frosty dark, far-faint, there was the departing wail of a whistle.

And suddenly, as he watched the lights wing cheerfully up in the town, their warm message of the hived life of men brought to him a numb hunger for all the words and the faces. He heard the far voices and laughter. And on the distant road a powerful car, bending around the curve, cast over him for a second, over that lonely hill of the dead, its great shaft of light and life. In his numbed mind, which for days now had fumbled curiously with little things, with little things alone, as a child fumbles with blocks or with little things, a light was growing.

His mind gathered itself out of the wreckage of little things: out of all that the world had shown or taught him he could remember now only the great star above the town, and the light that had swung over the hill, and the fresh sod upon Ben's grave, and the wind, and far sounds and music, and Mrs. Pert.

Wind pressed the boughs, the withered leaves were

shaking. It was October, but the leaves were shaking. A star
was shaking. A light was waking. Wind was quaking. The
star was far. The night, the light. The light was bright. A
chant, a song, the slow dance of the little things within him.
The star over the town, the light over the hill, the sod over
Ben, night over all. His mind fumbled with little things. Over
us all is something. Star, night, earth, light ... light ... O
lost! ... a stone ... a leaf ... a door ... O ghost! ... a light
... a song ... a light ... a light swings over the hill ... over
us all ... a star shines over the town ... over us all ... a
light.

We shall not come again. We never shall come back
again. But over us all, over us all, over us all is—something.

Wind pressed the boughs; the withered leaves were
shaking. It was October, but some leaves were shaking.

A light swings over the hill. (We shall not come
again.) And over the town a star. (Over us all, over us all
that shall not come again.) And over the day the dark. But
over the darkness—what?

We shall not come again. We never shall come back
again.

Over the dawn a lark. (That shall not come again.)
And wind and music far. O lost! (It shall not come again.)
And over your mouth the earth. O ghost! But, over the dark-
ness—what?

Wind pressed the boughs; the withered leaves were
quaking.

We shall not come again. We never shall come back
again. It was October, but we never shall come back again.

When will they come again? When will they come
again?

The laurel, the lizard, and the stone will come no

more. The women weeping at the gate have gone and will not come again. And pain and pride and death will pass, and will not come again. And light and dawn will pass, and the star and the cry of a lark will pass, and will not come again. And we shall pass, and shall not come again.

What things will come again? O Spring, the cruellest and fairest of the seasons, will come again. And the strange and buried men will come again, in flower and leaf the strange and buried men will come again, and death and the dust will never come again, for death and the dust will die. And Ben will come again, he will not die again, in flower and leaf, in wind and music far, he will come back again.

O lost, and by the wind grieved, ghost, come back again!

It had grown dark. The frosty night blazed with great brilliant stars. The lights in the town shone with sharp radiance. Presently, when he had lain upon the cold earth for some time, Eugene got up and went away toward the town.

Wind pressed the boughs; the withered leaves were shaking.

Sherwood Anderson (1876–1941)

Sherwood Anderson, a self-educated man, was born in Camden, Ohio. Regarded by many critics as one of the liberators of American literature, Anderson was associated with the Chicago Group of writers preceding and following World War I. He concerned himself with realistic psychological probing into the lives of bewildered, lonely and frustrated people, portraying the sterility of life in the small town and the impersonality of the big city. A seeker of a meaning in life, attempting to find some general truths in the complexities around him, Sherwood Anderson analyzed repressed individuals, "grotesques," who are crushed by the industrial age and by forces beyond their control and understanding. "Hands" is from Winesburg, Ohio, *a collection of sketches of small-town life and its warped personalities.*

HANDS

Upon the half-decayed veranda of a small frame house that stood near the edge of a ravine near the town of Winesburg, Ohio, a fat little old man walked nervously up and down. Across a long field that had been seeded for clover but that had produced only a dense crop of yellow mustard weeds, he could see the public highway along which went a wagon filled with berry-pickers returning from the fields. The berry-pickers, youths and maidens, laughed and shouted boisterously. A boy clad in a blue shirt leaped from the wagon and attempted to drag after him one of the maidens, who screamed and protested shrilly. The feet of the boy in the road kicked up a cloud of dust that floated across the face of the departing sun. Over the long field came a thin girlish voice. "Oh, you Wing Biddlebaum, comb your hair, it's falling into your eyes," commanded the voice to the man, who was bald and whose nervous little hands fiddled about the bare white forehead as though arranging a mass of tangled locks.

Wing Biddlebaum, forever frightened and beset by a ghostly band of doubts, did not think of himself as in any way a part of the life of the town where he had lived for twenty years. Among all the people of Winesburg but one had come close to him. With George Willard, son of Tom Willard, the proprietor of the new Willard House, he had formed something like a friendship. George Willard was the reporter on the *Winesburg Eagle* and sometimes in the evenings he walked out along the highway to Wing Biddlebaum's house. Now as the old man walked up and down the veranda, his hands moving nervously about, he was hoping that George Willard would come and spend the evening with him. After the wagon containing the berry-pickers had passed, he went across the field through the tall mustard weeds and climbing a rail fence peered anxiously along the road to the town. For a moment he stood thus, rubbing his hands together and looking up and down the road, and then, fear overcoming him, ran back to walk again upon the porch on his own house.

In the presence of George Willard, Wing Biddlebaum, who for twenty years had been the town mystery, lost something of his timidity, and his shadowy personality, submerged in a sea of doubts, came forth to look at the world. With the young reporter at his side, he ventured in the light of day into Main Street or strode up and down on the rickety front porch of his own house, talking excitedly. The voice that had been low and trembling became shrill and loud. The bent figure straightened. With a kind of wiggle, like a fish returned to the brook by the fisherman, Biddlebaum the silent began to talk, striving to put into words the ideas that had been accumulated by his mind during long years of silence.

Wing Biddlebaum talked much with his hands. The slender expressive fingers, forever active, forever striving to conceal themselves in his pockets or behind his back, came forth and became the piston rods of his machinery of expression.

The story of Wing Biddlebaum is a story of hands. Their restless activity, like unto the beating of the wings of an imprisoned bird, had given him his name. Some obscure poet of the town had thought of it. The hands alarmed their owner. He wanted to keep them hidden away and looked with amazement at the quiet inexpressive hands of other men who worked beside him in the fields, or passed, driving sleepy teams on country roads.

When he talked to George Willard, Wing Biddlebaum closed his fists and beat with them upon a table or on the walls of his house. The action made him more comfortable. If the desire to talk came to him when the two were walking in the fields, he sought out a stump or the top board of a fence and with his hands pounding busily talked with renewed ease.

The story of Wing Biddlebaum's hands is worth a book in itself. Sympathetically set forth it would tap many strange, beautiful qualities in obscure men. It is a job for a poet. In Winesburg the hands had attracted attention merely because of their activity. With them Wing Biddlebaum had picked as high as a hundred and forty quarts of strawberries in a day. They became his distinguishing feature, the source of his fame. Also they made more grotesque an already grotesque and elusive individuality. Winesburg was proud of the hands of Wing Biddlebaum in the same spirit in which it was proud of Banker White's new stone house and Wesley Moyer's bay stallion, Tony Tip, that had won the two-fifteen trot at the fall races in Cleveland.

As for George Willard, he had many times wanted to ask about the hands. At times an almost overwhelming curiosity had taken hold of him. He felt that there must be a reason for their strange activity and their inclination to keep hidden away, and only a growing respect for Wing Biddlebaum kept him from blurting out the questions that were often in his mind.

Once he had been on the point of asking. The two were walking in the fields on a summer afternoon and had stopped to sit upon a grassy bank. All afternoon Wing Biddlebaum had talked as one inspired. By a fence he had stopped and beating like a giant woodpecker upon the top board had shouted at George Willard, condemning his tendency to be too much influenced by the people about him. "You are destroying yourself," he cried. "You have the inclination to be alone and to dream and you are afraid of dreams. You want to be like others in town here. You hear them talk and you try to imitate them."

On the grassy bank Wing Biddlebaum had tried again to drive his point home. His voice became soft and reminiscent, and with a sigh of contentment he launched into a long rambling talk, speaking as one lost in a dream.

Out of the dream Wing Biddlebaum made a picture for George Willard. In the picture men lived again in a kind of pastoral golden age. Across a green open country came clean-limbed young men, some afoot, some mounted upon horses. In crowds the young men came to gather about the feet of an old man who sat beneath a tree in a tiny garden and who talked to them.

Wing Biddlebaum became wholly inspired. For once he forgot the hands. Slowly they stole forth and lay upon George Willard's shoulders. Something new and bold came into the voice that talked. "You must try to forget all you have learned," said the old man. "You must begin to dream. From this time on you must shut your ears to the roaring of the voices."

Pausing in his speech, Wing Biddlebaum looked long and earnestly at George Willard. His eyes glowed. Again he raised the hands to caress the boy and then a look of horror swept over his face.

With a convulsive movement of his body, Wing Biddlebaum sprang to his feet and thrust his hands deep into his trousers pockets. Tears came to his eyes. "I must be getting along home. I can talk no more with you," he said nervously.

Without looking back, the old man had hurried down the hillside and across a meadow, leaving George Willard perplexed and frightened upon the grassy slope. With a shiver of dread the boy arose and went along the road toward town.

"I'll not ask him about his hands," he thought, touched by the memory of the terror he had seen in the man's eyes. "There's something wrong, but I don't want to know what it is. His hands have something to do with his fear of me and of everyone."

And George Willard was right. Let us look briefly into the story of the hands. Perhaps our talking of them will arouse the poet who will tell the hidden wonder story of the influence for which the hands were but fluttering pennants of promise.

In his youth Wing Biddlebaum had been a school teacher in a town in Pennsylvania. He was not then known as Wing Biddlebaum, but went by the less euphonic name of Adolph Myers. As Adolph Myers he was much loved by the boys of his school.

Adolph Myers was meant by nature to be a teacher of youth. He was one of those rare, little-understood men who rule by a power so gentle that it passes as a lovable weakness. In their feeling for the boys under their charge, such men are not unlike the finer sort of women in their love of men.

And yet that is but crudely stated. It needs the poet there. With the boys of his school, Adolph Myers had walked in the evening or had sat talking until dusk upon the schoolhouse steps lost in a kind of dream. Here and there went his hands, carressing the shoulders of the boys, playing about the tousled heads. As he talked, his voice became soft and musical. There was a caress in that also. In a way the voice and the hands, the stroking of the shoulders and the touching of the hair, were a part of the schoolmaster's effort to carry a dream into the young minds. By the caress that was in his fingers he expressed himself. He was one of those men in

whom the force that creates life is diffused, not centralized.
Under the caress of his hands doubt and disbelief went out
of the minds of the boys and they began also to dream.

And then the tragedy. A half-witted boy of the school
became enamored of the young master. In his bed at night he
imagined unspeakable things and in the morning went forth
to tell his dreams as facts. Strange, hideous accusations fell
from his loose-hung lips. Through the Pennsylvania town
went a shiver. Hidden, shadowy doubts that had been in
men's minds concerning Adolph Myers were galvanized into
beliefs.

The tragedy did not linger. Trembling lads were jerked
out of bed and questioned. "He put his arms about me," said
one. "His fingers were always playing in my hair," said
another.

One afternoon a man of the town, Henry Bradford,
who kept a saloon, came to the schoolhouse door. Calling
Adolph Myers into the school yard he began to beat him with
his fists. As his hard knuckles beat down into the frightened
face of the schoolmaster, his wrath became more and more
terrible. Screaming with dismay, the children ran here and
there like disturbed insects. "I'll teach you to put your hands
on my boy, you beast," roared the saloonkeeper, who, tired
of beating the master, had begun to kick him about the yard.

Adolph Myers was driven from the Pennsylvania town
in the night. With lanterns in their hands a dozen men came
to the door of the house where he lived alone and commanded
that he dress and come forth. It was raining and one of the
men had a rope in his hands. They had intended to hang the
schoolmaster, but something in his figure, so small, white, and
pitiful, touched their hearts and they let him escape. As he
ran away into the darkness they repented of their weakness

and ran after him, swearing and throwing sticks and great balls of soft mud at the figure that screamed and ran faster and faster into the darkness.

For twenty years Adolph Myers had lived alone in Winesburg. He was but forty but looked sixty-five. The name of Biddlebaum he got from a box of goods seen at a freight station as he hurried through an eastern Ohio town. He had an aunt in Winesburg, a black-toothed old woman who raised chickens, and with her he lived until she died. He had been ill for a year after the experience in Pennsylvania, and after his recovery worked as a day laborer in the fields, going timidly about and striving to conceal his hands. Although he did not understand what had happened, he felt that the hands must be to blame. Again and again the fathers of the boys had talked of the hands. "Keep your hands to yourself," the saloonkeeper had roared, dancing with fury in the schoolhouse yard.

Upon the veranda of his house by the ravine, Wing Biddlebaum continued to walk up and down until the sun had disappeared and the road beyond the field was lost in the gray shadows. Going into his house he cut slices of bread and spread honey upon them. When the rumble of the evening train that took away the express cars loaded with the day's harvest of berries had passed and restored the silence of the summer night, he went again to walk upon the veranda. In the darkness he could not see the hands and they became quiet. Although he still hungered for the presence of the boy, who was the medium through which he expressed his love of man, the hunger became again a part of his loneliness and his waiting. Lighting a lamp, Wing Biddlebaum washed the few dishes soiled by his simple meal and, setting up a folding cot by the screen door that led to the porch, prepared to undress for the night. A few stray white bread crumbs lay on the cleanly washed floor by the table; putting the lamp upon a low stool he began to pick up the crumbs, carrying them to his mouth one by one with unbelievable rapidity. In the dense blotch of light beneath the table, the kneeling figure looked like a priest engaged in some service of his church. The nervous expressive fingers, flashing in and out of the light, might well have been mistaken for the fingers of the devotee going swiftly through decade after decade of his rosary.

Ring Lardner (1885–1933)

Ring Lardner accurately captured the speech rhythms and patterns, and the new words, of the time. Using realistic conversations with emphasis on the vernacular and slang, he created brutal caricatures and devastating satires to expose dullness and cruelty.

Lardner's ironic flair appeared in many of his stories as he questioned standardized viewpoints and values. For many years he was a reporter and sports writer in South Bend, Indiana; Chicago, Illinois; and St. Louis, Missouri. Born in Niles, Michigan, Ring Lardner attended the Armour Institute of Technology in Chicago.

HAIRCUT

I got another barber that comes over from Carterville and helps me out Saturdays, but the rest of the time I can get along all right alone. You can see for yourself that this ain't no New York City and besides that, the most of the boys works all day and don't have no leisure to drop in here and get themselves prettied up.

You're a newcomer, ain't you? I thought I hadn't seen

you round before. I hope you like it good enough to stay. As I say, we ain't no New York City or Chicago, but we have pretty good times. Not as good, though, since Jim Kendall got killed. When he was alive, him and Hod Meyers used to keep this town in an uproar. I bet they was more laughin' done here than any town its size in America.

Jim was comical, and Hod was pretty near a match for him. Since Jim's gone, Hod tries to hold his end up just the same as ever, but it's tough goin' when you ain't got nobody to kind of work with.

They used to be plenty fun here Saturdays. This place is jam-packed Saturdays, from four o'clock on. Jim and Hod would show up right after their supper, round six o'clock. Jim would set himself down in that big chair, nearest the blue spittoon. Whoever had been settin' in that chair, why they'd get up when Jim come in and give it to him.

You'd of thought it was a reserved seat like they have sometimes in a theayter. Hod would generally always stand or walk up and down, or some Saturdays, of course, he'd be settin' in this chair part of the time, gettin' a haircut.

Well, Jim would set there a w'ile without openin' his mouth only to spit, and then finally he'd say to me, "Whitey," —my right name, that is, my right first name, is Dick, but everybody round here calls me Whitey—Jim would say, "Whitey, your nose looks like a rosebud tonight. You must of been drinkin' some of your aw de cologne."

So I'd say, "No, Jim, but you look like you'd been drinkin' somethin' of that kind or somethin' worse."

Jim would have to laugh at that, but then he'd speak up and say, "No, I ain't had nothin' to drink, but that ain't sayin' I wouldn't like somethin'. I wouldn't even mind if it was wood alcohol."

Then Hod Meyers would say, "Neither would your wife." That would set everybody to laughin' because Jim and his wife wasn't on very good terms. She'd of divorced him only they wasn't no chance to get alimony and she didn't have no way to take care of herself and the kids. She couldn't never understand Jim. He *was* kind of rough, but a good fella at heart.

Him and Hod had all kinds of sport with Milt Sheppard. I don't suppose you've seen Milt. Well, he's got an Adam's apple that looks more like a mushmelon. So I'd be shavin' Milt and when I'd start to shave down here on his neck, Hod would holler, "Hey, Whitey, wait a minute! Before you cut into it, let's make up a pool and see who can guess closest to the number of seeds."

And Jim would say, "If Milt hadn't of been so hoggish, he'd of ordered a half a cantaloupe instead of a whole one and it might not of stuck in his throat."

All the boys would roar at this and Milt himself would force a smile, though the joke was on him. Jim certainly was a card!

There's his shavin' mug, settin' on the shelf, right next to Charley Vail's. "Charles M. Vail." That's the druggist. He comes in regular for his shave, three times a week. And Jim's is the cup next to Charley's. "James H. Kendall." Jim won't need no shavin' mug no more, but I'll leave it there just the same for old time's sake. Jim certainly was a character!

Years ago, Jim used to travel for a canned goods concern over in Carterville. They sold canned goods. Jim had the whole northern half of the State and was on the road five days out of every week. He'd drop in here Saturdays and tell his experiences for that week. It was rich.

I guess he paid more attention to playin' jokes than makin' sales. Finally the concern let him out and he come right home here and told everybody he'd been fired instead of sayin' he'd resigned like most fellas would of.

It was a Saturday and the shop was full and Jim got up out of that chair and says, "Gentlemen, I got an important announcement to make. I been fired from my job."

Well, they asked him if he was in earnest and he said he was and nobody could think of nothin' to say till Jim finally broke the ice himself. He says, "I been sellin' canned goods and now I'm canned goods myself."

You see, the concern he'd been workin' for was a factory that made canned goods. Over in Carterville. And now Jim said he was canned himself. He was certainly a card!

Jim had a great trick that he used to play w'ile he was travelin'. For instance, he'd be ridin' on a train and they'd come to some little town like, well, like, we'll say, like Benton. Jim would look out the train window and read the signs on the stores.

For instance, they'd be a sign, "Henry Smith, Dry Goods." Well, Jim would write down the name and the name of the town and when he got to wherever he was goin' he'd mail back a postal card to Henry Smith at Benton and not sign no name to it, but he'd write on the card, well, somethin' like "Ask your wife about that book agent that spent the afternoon last week," or "Ask your Missus who kept her from gettin' lonesome the last time you was in Carterville." And he'd sign the card, "A Friend."

Of course, he never knew what really come of none of these jokes, but he could picture what *probably* happened and that was enough.

Jim didn't work very steady after he lost his position

with the Carterville people. What he did earn, doin' odd jobs round town, why he spent pretty near all of it on gin and his family might of starved if the stores hadn't of carried them along. Jim's wife tried her hand at dressmakin', but they ain't nobody goin' to get rich makin' dresses in this town.

As I say, she'd of divorced Jim, only she seen that she couldn't support herself and the kids and she was always hopin' that some day Jim would cut out his habits and give her more than two or three dollars a week.

They was a time when she would go to whoever he was workin' for and ask them to give her his wages, but after she done this once or twice, he beat her to it by borrowin' most of his pay in advance. He told it all round town, how he had outfoxed his Missus. He certainly was a caution!

But he wasn't satisfied with just outwittin' her. He was sore the way she had acted, tryin' to grab off his pay. And he made up his mind he'd get even. Well, he waited till Evans's Circus was advertised to come to town. Then he told his wife and two kiddies that he was goin' to take them to the circus. The day of the circus, he told them he would get the tickets and meet them outside the entrance to the tent.

Well, he didn't have no intentions of bein' there or buyin' tickets or nothin'. He got full of gin and laid around Wright's poolroom all day. His wife and the kids waited and waited and of course he didn't show up. His wife didn't have a dime with her, or nowhere else, I guess. So she finally had to tell the kids it was all off and they cried like they wasn't never goin' to stop.

Well, it seems, w'ile they was cryin', Doc Stair came along and he asked what was the matter, but Mrs. Kendall was stubborn and wouldn't tell him, but the kids told him and he insisted on takin' them and their mother in the show. Jim found this out afterwards and it was one reason why he had it in for Doc Stair.

Doc Stair come here about a year and a half ago. He's a mighty handsome young fella and his clothes always look like he has them made to order. He goes to Detroit two or three times a year and w'ile he's there he must have a tailor take his measure and then make him a suit to order. They cost pretty near twice as much, but they fit a whole lot better than if you just bought them in a store.

For a w'ile everybody was wonderin' why a young doctor like Doc Stair should come to a town like this where we already got old Doc Gamble and Doc Foote that's both been here for years and all the practice in town was always divided between the two of them.

Then they was a story got round that Doc Stair's gal had throwed him over, a gal up in the Northern Peninsula somewheres, and the reason he come here was to hide himself away and forget it. He said himself that he thought they wasn't nothin' like general practice in a place like ours to fit a man to be a good all round doctor. And that's why he'd came.

Anyways, it wasn't long before he was makin' enough to live on, though they tell me that he never dunned nobody for what they owed him, and the folks here certainly has got the owin' habit, even in my business. If I had all that was comin' to me for just shaves alone, I could go to Carterville and put up at the Mercer for a week and see a different picture every night. For instance, they's old George Purdy—but I guess I shouldn't ought to be gossipin'.

Well, last year, our coroner died, died of the flu. Ken Beatty, that was his name. He was the coroner. So they had to choose another man to be coroner in his place and they picked Doc Stair. He laughed at first and said he didn't want it, but they made him take it. It ain't no job that anybody would fight for and what a man makes out of it in a year would just about buy seeds for their garden. Doc's the kind, though, that can't say no to nothin' if you keep at him long enough.

But I was goin' to tell you about a poor boy we got here in town—Paul Dickson. He fell out of a tree when he was about ten years old. Lit on his head and it done somethin' to him and he ain't never been right. No harm in him, but just silly. Jim Kendall used to call him cuckoo; that's a name Jim had for anybody that was off their head, only he called people's head their bean. That was another of his gags, callin' head bean and callin' crazy people cuckoo. Only poor Paul ain't crazy, but just silly.

You can imagine that Jim used to have all kinds of fun with Paul. He'd send him to the White Front Garage for a left-handed monkey wrench. Of course they ain't no such a thing as a left-handed monkey wrench.

And once we had a kind of a fair and they was a baseball game between the fats and the leans and before the game started Jim called Paul over and sent him way down to Schrader's hardware store to get a key for the pitcher's box.

They wasn't nothin' in the way of gags that Jim couldn't think up, when he put his mind to it.

Poor Paul was always kind of suspicious of people, maybe on account of how Jim had kept foolin' him. Paul wouldn't have much to do with anybody only his own mother and Doc Stair and a girl here in town named Julie Gregg. That is, she ain't a girl no more, but pretty near thirty or over.

When Doc first came to town, Paul seemed to feel like here was a real friend and he hung round Doc's office most of the w'ile; the only time he wasn't there was when he'd go home to eat or sleep or when he seen Julie Gregg doin' her shoppin'.

When he looked out Doc's window and seen her, he'd run downstairs and join her and tag along with her to the different stores. The poor boy was crazy about Julie and she always treated him mighty nice and made him feel like he was welcome, though of course it wasn't nothin' but pity on her side.

Doc done all he could to improve Paul's mind and he told me once that he really thought the boy was gettin' better, that they was times when he was as bright and sensible as anybody else.

But I was goin' to tell you about Julie Gregg. Old Man Gregg was in the lumber business, but got to drinkin' and lost the most of his money and when he died, he didn't leave nothin' but the house and just enough insurance for the girl to skimp along on.

Her mother was a kind of a half invalid and didn't hardly ever leave the house. Julie wanted to sell the place and move somewheres else after the old man died, but the mother said she was born here and would die here. It was tough on Julie, as the young people round this town—well, she's too good for them.

She's been away to school and Chicago and New York and different places and they ain't no subject she can't talk on, where you take the rest of the young folks here and you mention anything to them outside of Gloria Swanson or Tommy Meighan and they think you're delirious. Did you see Gloria in Wages of Virtue? You missed somethin'!

Well, Doc Stair hadn't been here more than a week when he come in one day to get shaved and I recognized who he was as he had been pointed out to me, so I told him about my old lady. She's ben ailin' for a couple of years and either Doc Gamble or Doc Foote, neither one, seemed to be helpin' her. So he said he would come out and see her, but if she was able to get out herself, it would be better to bring her to his office where he could make a completer examination.

So I took her to his office and w'ile I was waitin' for her in the reception room, in come Julie Gregg. When somebody comes in Doc Stair's office, they's a bell that rings in his inside office so as he can tell they's somebody to see him.

So he left my old lady inside and come out to the front office and that's the first time him and Julie met and I guess it was what they call love at first sight. But it wasn't fifty-fifty. This young fella was the slickest lookin' fella she'd ever seen in this town and she went wild over him. To him she was just a young lady that wanted to see the doctor.

She'd came on about the same business I had. Her mother had been doctorin' for years with Doc Gamble and Doc Foote and without no results. So she'd heard they was a new doc in town and decided to give him a try. He promised to call and see her mother that same day.

I said a minute ago that it was love at first sight on her part. I'm not only judgin' by how she acted afterwards but how she looked at him that first day in his office. I ain't no mind reader, but it was wrote all over her face that she was gone.

Now Jim Kendall, besides bein' a jokesmith and a pretty good drinker, well, Jim was quite a lady-killer. I guess he run pretty wild durin' the time he was on the road for them Carterville people, and besides that, he'd had a couple little affairs of the heart right here in town. As I say, his wife could of divorced him, only she couldn't.

But Jim was like the majority of men, and women, too,
I guess. He wanted what he couldn't get. He wanted Julie
Gregg and worked his head off tryin' to land her. Only he'd
of said bean instead of head.

Well, Jim's habits and his jokes didn't appeal to Julie
and of course he was a married man, so he didn't have no
more chance than, well, than a rabbit. That's an expression
of Jim's himself. When somebody didn't have no chance to
get elected or somethin', Jim would always say they didn't
have no more chance than a rabbit.

He didn't make no bones about how he felt. Right in
here, more than once, in front of the whole crowd, he said
he was stuck on Julie and anybody that could get her for
him was welcome to his house and his wife and kids included.
But she wouldn't have nothin' to do with him; wouldn't even
speak to him on the street. He finally seen he wasn't gettin'
nowheres with his usual line so he decided to try the rough
stuff. He went right up to her house one evenin' and when
she opened the door he forced his way in and grabbed her.
But she broke loose and before he could stop her, she run in
the next room and locked the door and phoned to Joe Barnes.
Joe's the marshal. Jim could hear who she was phonin' to
and he beat it before Joe got there.

Joe was an old friend of Julie's pa. Joe went to Jim the
next day and told him what would happen if he ever done it
again.

I don't know how the news of this little affair leaked
out. Chances is that Joe Barnes told his wife and she told
somebody else's wife and they told their husband. Anyways,
it did leak out and Hod Meyers had the nerve to kid Jim about
it, right here in this shop. Jim didn't deny nothin' and kind of

laughed it off and said for us all to wait; that lots of people had tried to make a monkey out of him, but he always got even.

Meanw'ile everybody in town was wise to Julie's bein' wild mad over the Doc. I don't suppose she had any idear how her face changed when him and her was together; of course she couldn't of, or she'd of kept away from him. And she didn't know that we was all noticin' how many times she made excuses to go up to his office or pass it on the other side of the street and look up in his window to see if he was there. I felt sorry for her and so did most other people.

Hod Meyers kept rubbin' it into Jim about how the Doc had cut him out. Jim didn't pay no attention to the kiddin' and you could see he was plannin' one of his jokes.

One trick Jim had was the knack of changin' his voice. He could make you think he was a girl talkin' and he could mimic any man's voice. To show you how good he was along this line, I'll tell you the joke he played on me once.

You know, in most towns of any size, when a man is dead and needs a shave, why the barber that shaves him soaks him five dollars for the job; that is, he don't soak *him*, but whoever ordered the shave. I just charge three dollars because personally I don't mind much shavin' a dead person. They lay a whole lot stiller than live customers. The only thing is that you don't feel like talkin' to them and you get kind of lonesome.

Well, about the coldest day we ever had here, two years ago last winter, the phone rung at the house w'ile I was home to dinner and I answered the phone and it was a woman's voice and she said she was Mrs. John Scott and her husband was dead and would I come out and shave him.

Old John had always been a good customer of mine. But they live seven miles out in the country, on the Streeter road. Still I didn't see how I could say no.

So I said I would be there, but would have to come in a jitney and it might cost three or four dollars besides the price of the shave. So she, or the voice, it said that was all right, so I got Frank Abbott to drive me out to the place and when I got there, who should open the door but old John himself! He wasn't no more dead than, well, than a rabbit.

It didn't take no private detective to figure out who had played me this little joke. Nobody could of thought it up but Jim Kendall. He certainly was a card!

I tell you this incident just to show you how he could disguise his voice and make you believe it was somebody else talkin'. I'd of swore it was Mrs. Scott had called me. Anyways, some woman.

Well, Jim waited till he had Doc Stair's voice down pat; then he went after revenge.

He called Julie up on a night when he knew Doc was over in Carterville. She never questioned but what it was Doc's voice. Jim said he must see her that night; he couldn't wait no longer to tell her somethin'. She was all excited and told him to come to the house. But he said he was expectin' an important long distance call and wouldn't she please forget her manners for once and come to his office. He said they couldn't nothin' hurt her and nobody would see her and he just *must* talk to her a little w'ile. Well, poor Julie fell for it.

Doc always keeps a night light in his office, so it looked to Julie like they was somebody there.

Meanw'ile Jim Kendall had went to Wright's pool-room, where they was a whole gang amusin' themselves.

The most of them had drank plenty of gin, and they was a rough bunch even when sober. They was always strong for Jim's jokes and when he told them to come with him and see some fun they give up their card games and pool games and followed along.

Doc's office is on the second floor. Right outside his door they's a flight of stairs leadin' to the floor above. Jim and his gang hid in the dark behind these stairs.

Well, Julie come up to Doc's door and rung the bell and they was nothin' doin'. She rung it again and she rung it seven or eight times. Then she tried the door and found it locked. Then Jim made some kind of a noise and she heard it and waited a minute, and then she says, "Is that you, Ralph?" Ralph is Doc's first name.

They was no answer and it must of come to her all of a sudden that she'd been bunked. She pretty near fell downstairs and the whole gang after her. They chased her all the way home, hollerin', "Is that you, Ralph?" and "Oh, Ralphie, dear, is that you?" Jim says he couldn't holler it himself, as he was laughin' too hard.

Poor Julie! She didn't show up here on Main Street for a long, long time afterward.

And of course Jim and his gang told everybody in town, everybody but Doc Stair. They was scared to tell him, and he might of never knowed only for Paul Dickson. The poor cuckoo, as Jim called him, he was here in the shop one night when Jim was still gloatin' yet over what he'd done to Julie. And Paul took in as much of it as he could understand and he run to Doc with the story.

It's a cinch Doc went up in the air and swore he'd make Jim suffer. But it was a kind of a delicate thing, because if it got out that he had beat Jim up, Julie was bound to hear of it and then she'd know that Doc knew and of course knowin' that he knew would make it worse for her than ever. He was goin' to do somethin', but it took a lot of figurin'.

Well, it was a couple days later when Jim was here in the shop again, and so was the cuckoo. Jim was goin' duck-shootin' the next day and had came in lookin' for Hod Meyers to go with him. I happened to know that Hod had went over to Carterville and wouldn't be home till the end of the week. So Jim said he hated to go alone and he guessed he would call it off. Then poor Paul spoke up and said if Jim would take him he would go along. Jim thought a w'ile and then he said, well, he guessed a half-wit was better than nothin'.

I suppose he was plottin' to get Paul out in the boat and play some joke on him, like pushin' him in the water. Anyways, he said Paul could go. He asked him had he ever shot a duck and Paul said no, he'd never even had a gun in his hands. So Jim said he could set in the boat and watch him and if he behaved himself, he might lend him his gun for a couple of shots. They made a date to meet in the mornin' and that's the last I seen of Jim alive.

Next mornin', I hadn't been open more than ten minutes when Doc Stair come in. He looked kind of nervous. He asked me had I seen Paul Dickson. I said no, but I knew where he was, out duck-shootin' with Jim Kendall. So Doc says that's what he had heard, and he couldn't understand it because Paul had told him he wouldn't never have no more to do with Jim as long as he lived.

He said Paul had told him about the joke Jim had played on Julie. He said Paul had asked him what he thought of the joke and the Doc had told him that anybody that would do a thing like that ought not to be let live.

I said it had been a kind of a raw thing, but Jim just couldn't resist no kind of a joke, no matter how raw. I said I thought he was all right at heart, but just bubblin' over with mischief. Doc turned and walked out.

At noon he got a phone call from old John Scott. The lake where Jim and Paul had went shootin' is on John's place. Paul had came runnin' up to the house a few minutes before and said they'd been an accident. Jim had shot a few ducks and then give the gun to Paul and told him to try his luck. Paul hadn't never handled a gun and he was nervous. He was shakin' so hard that he couldn't control the gun. He let fire and Jim sunk back in the boat, dead.

Doc Stair, bein' the coroner, jumped in Frank Abbott's flivver and rushed out to Scott's farm. Paul and old John was down on the shore of the lake. Paul had rowed the boat to shore, but they'd left the body in it, waitin' for Doc to come.

Doc examined the body and said they might as well fetch it back to town. They was no use leavin' it there or callin' a jury, as it was a plain case of accidental shootin'.

Personally I wouldn't never leave a person shoot a gun in the same boat I was in unless I was sure they knew somethin' about guns. Jim was a sucker to leave a new beginner have his gun, let alone a half-wit. It probably served Jim right, what he got. But still we miss him round here. He certainly was a card!

Comb it wet or dry?

Floyd Dell (1887 –   )

For many readers Floyd Dell was a symbol of the literary renaissance of the early twenties. He left his home town, Barry, Illinois, worked in a factory, and later became literary editor of a Chicago newspaper. He became associated first with the Chicago Group of writers, and later with the Provincetown Group in New York City, where he wrote about the Bohemian life in Greenwich Village. A playwright, radical, pacifist, poet, novelist and short-story writer, Dell expressed the idealism and disillusionment of the period. "The Blanket" represents the melancholy mood found in many of Floyd Dell's works.

THE BLANKET

Petey hadn't really believed that Dad would be doing it—sending Granddad away. "Away" was what they were calling it. Not until now could he believe it of Dad.

But here was the blanket that Dad had that day bought for him, and in the morning he'd be going away. And this was the last evening they'd be having together.

Dad was off seeing that girl he was to marry. He'd not be back till late, and they could sit up and talk.

It was a fine September night, with a silver moon riding high over the gully. When they'd washed up the supper dishes they went out on the shanty porch, the old man and the bit of a boy, taking their chairs. "I'll get me fiddle," said the old man, "and play ye some of the old tunes." But instead of the fiddle he brought out the blanket. It was a big, double blanket, red, with black cross stripes.

"Now, isn't that a fine blanket!" said the old man, smoothing it over his knees. "And isn't your father a kind man to be giving the old fellow a blanket like that to go away with? It cost something, it did—look at the wool of it! And warm it will be these cold winter nights to come. There'll be few blankets there the equal of this one!"

It was like Granddad to be saying that. He was trying to make it easier. He'd pretended all along it was he that was wanting to go away to the great brick building—the government place, where he'd be with so many other old fellows having the best of everything. . . . But Petey hadn't believed Dad would really do it, until this night when he brought home the blanket.

"Oh, yes, it's a fine blanket," said Petey, and got up and went into the shanty. He wasn't the kind to cry, and, besides, he was too old for that, being eleven. He'd just come in to fetch Granddad's fiddle.

The blanket slid to the floor as the old man took the fiddle and stood up. It was the last night they'd be having together. There wasn't any need to say, "Play all the old tunes." Granddad tuned up for a minute, and then said, "This is one you'll like to remember."

The silver moon was high overhead, and there was a gentle breeze playing down the gully. He'd never be hearing Granddad play like this again. It was as well Dad was moving into that new house, away from here. He'd not want, Petey wouldn't, to sit here on the old porch of fine evenings, with Granddad gone.

The tune changed. "Here's something gayer." Petey sat and stared out over the gully. Dad would marry that girl. Yes, that girl who'd kissed him and slobbered over him, saying she'd try to be a good mother to him, and all. . . . His chair creaked as he involuntarily gave his body a painful twist.

The tune stopped suddenly, and Granddad said: "It's a poor tune, except to be dancing to." And then: "It's a fine girl your father's going to marry. He'll be feeling young again, with a pretty wife like that. And what would an old fellow like me be doing around their house, getting in the way, an old nuisance, what with my talk of aches and pains! And then there'll be babies coming, and I'd not want to be there to hear them crying at all hours. It's best that I take myself off, like I'm doing. One more tune or two, and then we'll be going to bed to get some sleep against the morning, when I'll pack up my fine blanket and take my leave. Listen to this, will you? It's a bit sad, but a fine tune for a night like this."

They didn't hear the two people coming down the gully path, Dad and the pretty girl with the hard, bright face like a china doll's. But they heard her laugh, right by the porch, and the tune stopped on a wrong, high, startled note. Dad didn't say anything, but the girl came forward and spoke to Granddad prettily: "I'll not be seeing you leave in the morning, so I came over to say good-by."

"It's kind of you," said Granddad, with his eyes cast down; and then, seeing the blanket at his feet, he stopped to pick it up. "And will you look at this," he said in embarrassment, "the fine blanket my son has given me to go away with!"

"Yes," she said, "it's a fine blanket." She felt of the wool, and repeated in surprise, "A fine blanket—I'll say it is!" She turned to Dad, and said to him coldly, "It cost something, that."

He cleared his throat, and said defensively, "I wanted him to have the best. . . ."

The girl stood there, still intent on the blanket. "It's double, too," she said reproachfully to Dad.

"Yes," said Granddad, "it's double—a fine blanket for an old fellow to be going away with."

The boy went abruptly into the shanty. He was looking for something. He could hear that girl reproaching Dad, and Dad becoming angry in his slow way. And now she was suddenly going away in a huff. . . . As Petey came out, she turned and called back, "All the same, he doesn't need a double blanket!" And she ran up the gully path.

Dad was looking after her uncertainly.

"Oh, she's right," said the boy coldly. "Here, Dad" —and he held out a pair of scissors. "Cut the blanket in two."

Both of them stared at the boy, startled. "Cut it in two, I tell you, Dad!" he cried out. "And keep the other half!"

"That's not a bad idea," said Granddad gently. "I don't need so much of a blanket."

"Yes," said the boy harshly, "a single blanket's enough for an old man when he's sent away. We'll save the other half, Dad; it will come in handy later."

"Now, what do you mean by that?" asked Dad.

"I mean," said the boy slowly, "that I'll give it to you, Dad—when you're old and I'm sending you—away."

There was a silence, and then Dad went over to Granddad and stood before him, not speaking. But Granddad understood, for he put out a hand and laid it on Dad's shoulder. Petey was watching them. And he heard Granddad whisper, "It's all right, son—I knew you didn't mean it...." And then Petey cried.

But it didn't matter—because they were all three crying together.

Sinclair Lewis (1885–1951)

Awarded the Nobel Prize in Literature (1930) for Main Street, Babbitt and Arrowsmith, as well as a Pulitzer Prize (1926) for Arrowsmith, Sinclair Lewis satirized the shortcomings of middle-class life. Through the novel and short story he realistically exposed the illusions of society with savage portraits of vulgar small-town existence and with bitter attacks on complacency and dullness, on the spiritual failure of Americans and on social conformity.

Sinclair Lewis was born and raised in Sauk Center, Minnesota, and was graduated from Yale. In the opening chapter of Babbitt he ridicules smugness and the measurement of success by wealth, and the businessman's narrow views.

FROM BABBITT

I

The towers of Zenith aspired above the morning mist; austere towers of steel and cement and limestone, sturdy as cliffs and delicate as silver rods. They were neither citadels nor churches, but frankly and beautifully office buildings.

The mist took pity on the fretted structures of earlier generations: the Post Office with its shingle-tortured mansard, the red brick minarets of hulking old houses, factories with stingy and sooted windows, wooden tenements colored like mud. The city was full of such grotesqueries, but the clean towers were thrusting them from the business center, and on the farther hills were shining new houses, homes—they seemed—for laughter and tranquillity.

Over a concrete bridge fled a limousine of long sleek hood and noiseless engine. These people in evening clothes were returning from an all-night rehearsal of a Little Theater play, an artistic adventure considerably illuminated by champagne. Below the bridge curved a railroad, a maze of green and crimson lights. The New York Flyer boomed past, and twenty lines of polished steel leaped into the glare.

In one of the skyscrapers the wires of the Associated Press were closing down. The telegraph operators wearily raised their celluloid eyeshades after a night of talking with Paris and Peking. Through the building crawled the scrubwomen, yawning, their old shoes slapping. The dawn mist spun away. Cues of men with lunch boxes clumped toward the immensity of new factories, sheets of glass and hollow tile, glittering shops where five thousand men worked beneath one roof, pouring out the honest wares that would be sold up the Euphrates and across the veldt. The whistles rolled out in greeting a chorus cheerful as the April dawn; the song of labor in a city built—it seemed—for giants.

II

There was nothing of the giant in the aspect of the man who was beginning to awaken on the sleeping porch of a Dutch Colonial house in that residential district of Zenith known as Floral Heights.

His name was George F. Babbitt. He was forty-six years old now, in April, 1920, and he made nothing in particular, neither butter nor shoes nor poetry, but he was nimble in the calling of selling houses for more than people could afford to pay.

His large head was pink, his brown hair thin and dry. His face was babyish in slumber, despite his wrinkles and the red spectacle dents on the slopes of his nose. He was not fat but he was exceedingly well fed; his cheeks were pads, and the unroughened hand which lay helpless upon the khaki-colored blanket was slightly puffy. He seemed prosperous, extremely married and unromantic; and altogether unromantic appeared this sleeping porch, which looked on one sizable elm, two respectable grassplots, a cement driveway, and a corrugated iron garage. Yet Babbitt was again dreaming of the fairy child, a dream more romantic than scarlet pagodas by a silver sea.

For years the fairy child had come to him. Where others saw but Georgie Babbitt, she discerned gallant youth. She waited for him, in the darkness beyond mysterious groves. When at last he could slip away from the crowded house he darted to her. His wife, his clamoring friends, sought to follow, but he escaped, the girl fleet besides him, and they crouched together on a shadowy hillside. She was so slim, so white, so eager! She cried that he was gay and valiant, that she would wait for him, that they would sail—

Rumble and bang of the milk truck.

Babbitt moaned, turned over, struggled back toward his dream. He could see only her face now, beyond misty waters. The furnace man slammed the basement door. A dog barked in the next yard. As Babbitt sank blissfully into a dim warm tide, the paper-carrier went by whistling, and the rolled-up *Advocate* thumped the front door. Babbit roused, his stomach constricted with alarm. As he relaxed, he was pierced by the familiar and irritating rattle of some one cranking a Ford: snap-ah-ah, snap-ah-ah, snap-ah-ah. Himself a pious motorist, Babbitt cranked with the unseen driver, with him waited through taut hours for the roar of the starting engine, with him agonized as the roar ceased and again began the infernal patient snap-ah-ah—a round, flat sound, a shivering cold-morning sound, a sound infuriating and inescapable. Not till the rising voice of the motor told him that the Ford was moving was he released from the panting tension. He glanced once at his favorite tree, elm twigs against the gold patina of sky, and fumbled for sleep as for a drug. He who had been a boy very credulous of life was no longer greatly interested in the possible and improbable adventures of each new day.

He escaped from reality till the alarm clock rang, at seven-twenty.

III

It was the best of nationally advertised and quantitatively produced alarm clocks, with all modern attachments, including cathedral chime, intermittent alarm, and a phosphorescent dial. Babbit was proud of being awakened by such a rich device. Socially it was almost as creditable as buying expensive cord tires.

He sulkily admitted now that there was no more escape, but he lay and detested the grind of the real-estate business, and disliked his family, and disliked himself for disliking them. The evening before, he had played poker at Vergil Gunch's till midnight, and after such holidays he was irritable before breakfast. It may have been the tremendous home-brewed beer of the prohibition era and the cigars to which that beer enticed him; it may have been resentment of return from this fine, bold man-world to a restricted region of wives and stenographers, and of suggestions not to smoke so much.

From the bedroom beside the sleeping porch, his wife's detestably cheerful "Time to get up, Georgie boy," and the itchy sound, the brisk and scratchy sound, of combing hairs out of a stiff brush.

He grunted; he dragged his thick legs, in faded baby-blue pajamas, from under the khaki blanket; he sat on the edge of the cot, running his fingers through his wild hair, while his plump feet mechanically felt for his slippers. He looked regretfully at the blanket—forever a suggestion to him of freedom and heroism. He had bought it for a camping trip which had never come off. It symbolized gorgeous loafing, gorgeous cursing, virile flannel shirts.

He creaked to his feet, groaning at the waves of pain which passed behind his eyeballs. Though he waited for their scorching recurrence, he looked blurrily out at the yard. It delighted him, as always; it was the neat yard of a successful business man of Zenith, that is, it was perfection, and made him also perfect. He regarded the corrugated iron garage. For the three-hundred-and-sixty-fifth time in a year he reflected, "No class to that tin shack. Have to build me a frame garage. But by golly it's the only thing on the place that isn't up-to-date!" While he stared he thought of a community garage for his acreage development, Glen Oriole. He stopped puffing and jiggling. His arms were akimbo. His petulant, sleep-swollen face was set in harder lines. He suddenly seemed capable, an official, a man to contrive, to direct, to get things done.

On the vigor of his idea he was carried down the hard, clean, unused-looking hall into the bathroom.

Though the house was not large it had, like all houses on Floral Heights, an altogether royal bathroom of porcelain and glazed tile and metal sleek as silver. The towel rack was a rod of clear glass set in nickel. The tub was long enough for a Prussian Guard, and above the set bowl was a sensational exhibit of toothbrush holder, shaving-brush holder, soap dish, sponge dish, and medicine cabinet, so glittering and so ingenious that they resembled an electrical instrument board. But the Babbitt whose god was Modern Appliances was not pleased. The air of the bathroom was thick with the smell of a heathen toothpaste. "Verona been at it again! 'Stead of sticking to Lilidol, like I've re-peat-ed-ly asked her, she's gone and gotten some confounded stinkum stuff that makes you sick!"

The bath mat was wrinkled and the floor was wet. (His daughter Verona eccentrically took baths in the morning, now and then.) He slipped on the mat, and slid against the tub. He said "Damn!" Furiously he snatched up his tube of shaving cream, furiously he lathered, with a belligerent slapping of the unctuous brush, furiously he raked his plump cheeks with a safety razor. It pulled. The blade was dull. He said, "Damn—oh—oh—damn it!"

He hunted through the medicine cabinet for a packet of new razor blades (reflecting, as invariably, "Be cheaper to buy one of these dinguses and strop your own blades,") and when he discovered the packet, behind the round box of bicarbonate of soda, he thought ill of his wife for putting it there and very well of himself for not saying "Damn." But he did say it, immediately afterward, when with wet and soap-slippery fingers he tried to remove the horrible little envelope and crisp clinging oiled paper from the new blade.

Then there was the problem, oft-pondered, never solved, of what to do with the old blade, which might imperil the fingers of his young. As usual, he tossed it on top of the medicine cabinet, with a mental note that some day he must remove the fifty or sixty other blades that were also temporarily, piled up there. He finished his shaving in a growing testiness increased by his spinning headache and by the emptiness in his stomach. When he was done, his round face smooth and streamy and his eyes stinging from soapy water, he reached for a towel. The family towels were wet, wet and clammy and vile, all of them wet, he found, as he blindly snatched them—his own face towel, his wife's, Verona's, Ted's, Tinka's, and the lone bath towel with the huge welt of initial. Then George F. Babbitt did a dismaying thing. He wiped his face on the guest towel! It was a pansy-embroidered trifle which always hung there to indicate that the Babbitts were in the best Floral Heights society. No one had ever used it. No guest had ever dared to. Guests secretively took a corner of the nearest regular towel.

He was raging, "By golly, here they go and use up all the towels, every doggone one of' em, and they use 'em and get 'em all wet and sopping, and never put out a dry one for me—of course, I'm the goat!—and then I want one and—I'm the only person in the doggone house that's got the slightest doggone bit of consideration for other people and thoughtfulness and consider there may be others that may want to use the doggone bathroom after me and consider—"

He was pitching the chill abominations into the bathtub, pleased by the vindictiveness of that desolate flapping sound; and in the midst his wife serenely trotted in, observed serenely, "Why Georgie dear, what are you doing? Are you going to wash out the towels? Why, you needn't wash out the towels. Oh, Georgie, you didn't go and use the guest towel, did you?"

It is not recorded that he was able to answer.

For the first time in weeks he was sufficiently roused by his wife to look at her.

IV

Myra Babbitt—Mrs. George F. Babbitt—was definitely mature. She had creases from the corners of her mouth to the bottom of her chin, and her plump neck bagged. But the thing that marked her as having passed the line was that she no longer had reticences before her husband, and no longer worried about not having reticences. She was in a petticoat now, and corsets which bulged, and unaware of being seen in bulgy corsets. She had become so dully habituated to married life that in her full matronliness she was as sexless as an anemic nun. She was a good woman, a kind woman, a diligent woman, but no one, save perhaps Tinka her ten-year-old, was at all interested in her or entirely aware that she was alive.

After a rather thorough discussion of all the domestic and social aspects of towels she apologized to Babbitt for his having an alcoholic headache; and he recovered enough to endure the search for a B.V.D. undershirt which had, he pointed out, malevolently been concealed among his clean pajamas.

He was fairly amiable in the conference on the brown suit.

"What do you think, Myra?" He pawed at the clothes hunched on a chair in their bedroom, while she moved about mysteriously adjusting and patting her petticoat and, to his jaundiced eye, never seeming to get on with her dressing. "How about it? Shall I wear the brown suit another day?"

"Well, it looks awfully nice on you."

"I know, but gosh, it needs pressing."

"That's so. Perhaps it does."

"It certainly could stand being pressed, all right."

"Yes, perhaps it wouldn't hurt it to be pressed."

"But gee, the coat doesn't need pressing. No sense in having the whole darn suit pressed, when the coat doesn't need it."

"That's so."

"But the pants certainly need it, all right. Look at them—look at those wrinkles—the pants certainly do need pressing."

"That's so. Oh, Georgie, why couldn't you wear the brown coat with the blue trousers we were wondering what we'd do with them?"

"Good Lord! Did you ever in all my life know me to wear the coat of one suit and the pants of another? What do you think I am? A busted bookkeeper?"

"Well, why don't you put on the dark gray suit today, and stop in at the tailor and leave the brown trousers?"

"Well, they certainly need— Now where the devil is that gray suit? Oh, yes, here we are."

He was able to get through the other crises of dressing with comparative resoluteness and calm.

His first adornment was the sleeveless dimity B.V.D. undershirt, in which he resembled a small boy humorlessly wearing a cheesecloth tabard at a civic pageant. He never put on B.V.D.'s without thanking the God of Progress that he didn't wear tight, long, old-fashioned undergarments, like his father-in-law and partner, Henry Thompson. His second embellishment was combing and slicking back his hair. It gave him a tremendous forehead, arching up two inches beyond the former hairline. But most wonder-working of all was the donning of his spectacles.

There is character in spectacles—the pretentious tortoiseshell, the meek pince-nez of the schoolteacher, the twisted silver-framed glasses of the old villager. Babbitt's spectacles had huge, circular, frameless lenses of the very best glass; the earpieces were thin bars of gold. In them he was the modern businessman; one who gave orders to clerks and drove a car and played occasional golf and was scholarly in regard to Salesmanship. His head suddenly appeared not babyish but weighty, and you noted his heavy, blunt nose, his straight mouth and thick, long upper lip, his chin overfleshy but strong; with respect you beheld him put on the rest of his uniform as a Solid Citizen.

The gray suit was well cut, well made, and completely undistinguished. It was a standard suit. White piping on the V of the vest added a flavor of law and learning. His shoes were black laced boots, good boots, honest boots, standard boots, extraordinarily uninteresting boots. The only frivolity was in his purple knitted scarf. With considerable comment on the matter to Mrs. Babbitt (who, acrobatically fastening the back of her blouse to her skirt with a safety pin, did not hear a word he said), he chose between the purple scarf and a tapestry effect with stringless brown harps among blown palms, and into it he thrust a snakehead pin with opal eyes.

A sensational event was changing from the brown suit to the gray the contents of his pockets. He was earnest about these objects. They were of eternal importance, like baseball or the Republican Party. They included a fountain pen and a silver pencil (always lacking a supply of new leads) which belonged in the right-hand upper vest pocket. Without them he would have felt naked. On his watch chain were a gold penknife, silver cigar-cutter, seven keys (the use of two of which he had forgotten), and incidentally a good watch. Depending from the chain was a large, yellowish elk's tooth —proclamation of his membership in the Brotherly and Protective Order of Elks. Most significant of all was his loose-leaf pocket notebook, that modern and efficient notebook which contained the addresses of people whom he had forgotten, prudent memoranda of postal money orders which had reached their destinations months ago, stamps which had lost their mucilage, clippings of verses by T. Cholmondeley Frink and of the newspaper editorials from which Babbitt got his opinions and his polysyllables, notes to be sure and do things which he did not intend to do, and one curious inscription—D.S.S.D.M.Y.P.D.F.

But he had no cigarette case. No one had ever happened to give him one, so he hadn't the habit, and people who carried cigarette cases he regarded as effeminate.

Last, he stuck in his lapel the Boosters' Club button. With the conciseness of great art the button displayed two words: "Boosters—Pep!" It made Babbitt feel loyal and important. It associated him with Good Fellows, with men who were nice and human, and important in business circles.

It was his V.C., his Legion of Honor ribbon, his Phi Beta Kappa key.

With the subtleties of dressing ran other complex worries. "I feel kind of punk this morning," he said. "I think I had too much dinner last evening. You oughtn't to serve those heavy banana fritters."

"But you asked me to have some."

"I know, but— I tell you, when a fellow gets past forty he has to look after his digestion. There's a lot of fellows that don't take proper care of themselves. I tell you at forty a man's a fool or his doctor—I mean, his own doctor. Folks don't give enough attention to this matter of dieting. Now I think— Course a man ought to have a good meal after the day's work, but it would be a good thing for both of us if we took lighter lunches."

"But Georgie, here at home I always do have a light lunch."

"Mean to imply I make a hog of myself, eating downtown? Yes, sure! You'd have a swell time if you had to eat the truck that new steward hands out to us at the Athletic Club! But I certainly do feel out of sorts, this morning. Funny, got a pain down here on the left side—but no, that wouldn't be appendicitis, would it? Last night, when I was driving over to Verg Grunch's, I felt a pain in my stomach, too. Right here it was—kind of a sharp shooting pain. I— Where'd that dime go to? Why don't you serve more prunes at breakfast? Of course I eat an apple every evening—an apple a day keeps the doctor away—but still, you ought to have more prunes, and not all these fancy doodads."

"The last time I had prunes you didn't eat them."

"Well, I didn't feel like eating 'em, I suppose. Matter of fact, I think I did eat some of 'em. Anyway— I tell you it's mighty important to— I was saying to Verg Gunch, just last evening, most people don't take sufficient care of their diges—"

"Shall we have the Gunches for our dinner, next week?"

"Why sure; you bet."

"Now see here, George: I want you to put on your nice dinner jacket that evening."

"Rats! The rest of 'em won't want to dress."

"Of course they will. You remember when you didn't dress for the Littlefields' supper party, and all the rest did, and how embarrassed you were."

"Embarrassed, hell! I wasn't embarrassed. Everybody knows I can put on as expensive a Tux. as anybody else, and I should worry if I don't happen to have it on sometimes. All a darn nuisance, anyway. All right for a woman, that stays around the house all the time, but when a fellow's worked like the dickens all day, he doesn't want to go and hustle his head off getting into the soup-and-fish for a lot of folks that he's seen in just reg'lar ordinary clothes that same day."

"You know you enjoy being seen in one. The other evening you admitted you were glad I'd insisted on your dressing. You said you felt a lot better for it. And oh, Georgie, I do wish you wouldn't say 'Tux.' It's 'dinner jacket.'"

"Rats, what's the odds?"

"Well, it's what all the nice folks say. Suppose Lucile McKelvey heard you calling it a 'Tux.'"

"Well, that's all right now! Lucile McKelvey can't pull anything on me! Her folks are common as mud, even if her husband and her dad are millionaires! I suppose you're trying to rub in *your* exalted social position! Well, let me tell you that your revered paternal ancestor, Henry T., doesn't even call it a 'Tux.'! He calls it a bobtail jacket for a ringtail monkey,' and you couldn't get him into one unless you chloroformed him!"

"Now don't be horrid, George."

"Well, I don't want to be horrid, but Lord! you're getting as fussy as Verona. Ever since she got out of college she's been too rambunctious to live with—doesn't know what she wants—well, I know what she wants!—all she wants is to marry a millionaire, and live in Europe, and hold some preacher's hand, and simultaneously at the same time stay right here in Zenith and be some blooming kind of a socialist agitator or boss charity worker or some damn thing! Lord, and Ted is just as bad! He wants to go college, and he doesn't want to go to college. Only one of the three that knows her own mind is Tinka. Simply can't understand how I ever came to have a pair of shilly-shallying children like Rone and Ted. I may not be any Rockefeller or James J. Shakespeare, but I certainly do know my own mind, and I do keep right on plugging along in the office and— Do you know the latest? Far as I can figure out, Ted's new bee is he'd like to be a movie actor and— And here I've told him a hundred times, if he'll go to college and law school and make good, I'll set him up in business and— Verona just exactly as bad. Doesn't know what she wants. Well, well, come on! Aren't you ready yet? The girl rang the bell three minutes ago."

V

Before he followed his wife, Babbitt stood at the westernmost window of their room. This residential settlement, Floral Heights, was on a rise; and though the center of the city was three miles away—Zenith had between three and four hundred thousand inhabitants now—he could see the top of the Second National Tower, an Indiana limestone building of thirty-five stories.

Its shining walls rose against April sky to a simple cornice like a streak of white fire. Integrity was in the tower, and decision. It bore its strength lightly as a tall soldier. As Babbitt stared, the nervousness was soothed from his face, his slack chin lifted in reverence. All he articulated was "That's one lovely sight!" but he was inspired by the rhythm of the city; his love of it renewed. He beheld the tower as a temple spire of the religion of business, a faith passionate, exalted, surpassing common men; and as he clumped down to breakfast he whistled the ballad "Oh, by gee, by gosh, by jingo" as though it were a hymn melancholy and noble.

Theodore Dreiser (1871–1935)

Theodore Dreiser has been described as the major voice of naturalistic frankness in the twenties. He was born in Terre Haute, Indiana, and attended the University of Indiana for one year. Through his fiction and essays, he protested the direction of society toward a ruthless, acquisitive materialism; he indicted America as hypocritical because of its claims as a humane society. Dreiser asserted that in reality the United States followed a code of brutal expediency causing moral breakdown and resultant misery for many people. He believed that environment dominates man, and as he searched for an understanding of the forces that determine man's existence he concluded that man must inevitably succumb to the environmental and biological forces. "The Second Choice" is representative of Theodore Dreiser's belabored style and his point of view.

THE SECOND CHOICE

SHIRLEY DEAR:

You don't want the letters. There are only six of them, anyhow, and think, they're all I have of you to cheer me

154

on my travels. What good would they be to you—little bits of notes telling me you're sure to meet me—but me—think of me! If I send them to you, you'll tear them up, whereas if you leave them with me I can dab them with musk and ambergris and keep them in a little silver box, always beside me.

Ah, Shirley dear, you really don't know how sweet I think you are, how dear! There isn't a thing we have ever done together that isn't as clear in my mind as this great big skyscraper over the way here in Pittsburgh, and far more pleasing. In fact, my thoughts of you are the most precious and delicious things I have, Shirley.

But I'm too young to marry now. You know that, Shirley, don't you? I haven't placed myself in any way yet, and I'm so restless that I don't know whether I ever will, really. Only yesterday, old Roxbaum—that's my new employer here—came to me and wanted to know if I would like an assistant overseership on one of his coffee plantations in Java, said there would not be much money in it for a year or two, a bare living, but later there would be more— and I jumped at it. Just the thought of Java and going there did that, although I knew I could make more staying right here. Can't you see how it is with me, Shirl? I'm too restless and too young. I couldn't take care of you right, and you wouldn't like me after a while if I didn't.

But ah, Shirley sweet, I think the dearest things of you! There isn't an hour, it seems, but some little bit of you comes back—a dear, sweet bit—the night we sat on the grass in Tregore Park and counted the stars through the trees; that first evening at Sparrows Point when we missed the last train and had to walk to Langley. Remember the tree toads, Shirl? And then that warm April Sunday in

Atholby woods! Ah, Shirl, you don't want the six notes!
Let me keep them. But think of me, will you, sweet, wherever
you go and whatever you do? I'll always think of you, and
wish that you had met a better, saner man than me, and that
I really could have married you and been all you wanted me
to be. By-by, sweet. I may start for Java within the month.
If so, and you would want them, I'll send you some cards
from there—if they have any.

Your worthless
ARTHUR

She sat and turned the letter in her hand, dumb with
despair. It was the very last letter she would ever get from
him. Of that she was certain. He was gone now, once and for
all. She had written him only once, not making an open plea
but asking him to return her letters, and then there had come
this tender but evasive reply, saying nothing of a possible return but desiring to keep her letters for old times' sake—
the happy hours they had spent together.

The happy hours! Oh, yes, yes, yes—the happy hours!

In her memory now, as she sat here in her home after
the day's work, meditating on all that had been in the few
short months since he had come and gone, was a world of
color and light—a color and light so transfiguring as to seem
celestial, but now, alas, wholly dissipated. It had contained
so much of all she had desired—love, romance, amusement,
laughter. He had been so gay and thoughtless, or headstrong,
so youthfully romantic, and with such a love of play and
change and to be saying and doing anything and everything.
Arthur could dance in a gay way, whistle, sing after a fashion, play. He could play cards and do tricks, and he had such
a superior air, so genial and brisk, with a kind of innate

courtesy in it and yet an intolerance for slowness and stodgi-
ness or anything dull or dingy, such as characterized—but
here her thoughts fled from him. She refused to think of any
one but Arthur.

Sitting in her little bedroom now, off the parlor on the
ground floor in her home in Bethune Street, and looking out
over the Kessels' yard, and beyond that—there being no
fences in Bethune Street—over the "yards" or lawns of the
Pollards, Bakers, Cryders and others, she thought of how
dull it must all have seemed to him, with his fine imaginative
mind and experiences, his love of change and gaiety, his
atmosphere of something better than she had ever known.
How little she had been fitted, perhaps, by beauty or tempera-
ment to overcome this—the something—dullness in her work
or her home, which possibly had driven him away. For, although many had admired her to date, and she was young
and pretty in her simple way and constantly receiving suggestions that her beauty was disturbing to some, he had not
cared for her—he had gone.

And now, as she meditated, it seemed that this scene,
and all that it stood for—her parents, her work, her daily
shuttling to and fro between the drug company for which
she worked and this street and house—was typical of her life
and what she was destined to endure always. Some girls
were so much more fortunate. They had fine clothes, fine
homes, a world of pleasure and opportunity in which to
move. They did not have to scrimp and save and work to pay
their own way. And yet she had always been compelled to
do it, but had never complained until now—or until he came,
and after. Bethune Street, with its commonplace front yards
and houses nearly all alike, and this house, so like the others,
room for room and porch for porch, and her parents, too,

really like all the others, had seemed good enough, quite satisfactory, indeed, until then. But now, now!

Here, in their kitchen, was her mother, a thin, pale, but kindly woman, peeling potatoes and washing lettuce, and putting a bit of steak or a chop or a piece of liver in a frying pan day after day, morning and evening, month after month, year after year. And next door was Mrs. Kessel doing the same thing. And next door Mrs. Cryder. And next door Mrs. Pollard. But, until now, she had not thought it so bad. But now—now—oh! And on all the porches or lawns all along this street were the husbands and fathers, mostly middle-aged or old men like her father, reading their papers or cutting the grass before dinner, or smoking and meditating afterward. Her father was out in front now, a stooped, forbearing, meditative soul, who had rarely anything to say—leaving it all to his wife, her mother, but who was fond of her in his dull, quiet way. He was a patternmaker by trade, and had come into possession of this small, ordinary home via years of toil and saving, her mother helping him. They had no particular religion, as he often said, thinking reasonably human conduct a sufficient passport to heaven, but they had gone occasionally to the Methodist Church over in Nicholas Street, and she had once joined it. But of late she had not gone, weaned away by the other commonplace pleasures of her world.

And then in the midst of it, the dull drift of things, as she now saw them to be, he had come—Arthur Bristow—young, energetic, good-looking, ambitious, dreamful, and instanter, and with her never knowing quite how, the whole thing had been changed. He had appeared so swiftly—out of nothing, as it were.

Previous to him had been Barton Williams, stout,

phlegmatic, good-natured, well-meaning, who was, or had been before Arthur came, asking her to marry him, and whom she allowed to half assume that she would. She had liked him in a feeble, albeit, as she thought, tender way, thinking him the kind, according to the logic of her neighborhood, who would make her a good husband, and, until Arthur appeared on the scene, had really intended to marry him. It was not really a love match, as she saw now, but she thought it was, which was much the same thing, perhaps. But, as she now recalled, when Arthur came, how the scales fell from her eyes! In a trice, as it were, nearly, there was a new heaven and a new earth. Arthur had arrived, and with him a sense of something different.

Mabel Gove had asked her to come over to her house in Westleigh, the adjoining suburb, for Thanksgiving eve and day, and without a thought of anything, and because Barton was busy handling a part of the work in the despatcher's office of the Great Eastern and could not see her, she had gone. And then, to her surprise and strange, almost ineffable delight, the moment she had seen him, he was there —Arthur, with his slim, straight figure and dark hair and eyes and clean-cut features, as clean and attractive as those of a coin. And as he had looked at her and smiled and narrated humorous bits of things that had happened to him, something had come over her—a spell—and after dinner they had all gone around to Edith Barringer's to dance, and there as she had danced with him, somehow, without any seeming boldness on his part, he had taken possession of her, as it were, drawn her close, and told her she had beautiful eyes and hair and such a delicately rounded chin, and that he thought she danced gracefully and was sweet. She had nearly fainted with delight.

"Do you like me?" he had asked in one place in the dance, and, in spite of herself, she had looked up into his eyes, and from that moment she was almost mad over him, could think of nothing else but his hair and eyes and his smile and his graceful figure.

Mabel Gove had seen it all, in spite of her determination that no one should, and on their going to bed later, back at Mabel's home, she had whispered:

"Ah, Shirley, I saw. You like Arthur, don't you?"

"I think he's very nice," Shirley recalled replying, for Mabel knew of her affair with Barton and liked him, "but I'm not crazy over him." And for this bit of treason she had sighed in her dreams nearly all night.

And the next day, true to a request and a promise made by him, Arthur had called again at Mabel's to take her and Mabel to a "movie" which was not so far away, and from there they had gone to an ice-cream parlor, and during it all, when Mabel was not looking, he had squeezed her arm and hand and kissed her neck, and she had held her breath, and her heart seemed to stop.

"And now you're going to let me come out to your place to see you, aren't you?" he had whispered.

And she had replied, "Wednesday evening," and then written the address on a little piece of paper and given it to him.

But now it was all gone, gone!

This house, which now looked so dreary—how romantic it had seemed that first night *he* called—the front room with its commonplace furniture, and later in the spring, the veranda, with its vines just sprouting, and the moon in May. Oh, the moon in May, and June and July, when he was here! How she had lied to Barton to make evenings for

Arthur, and occasionally to Arthur to keep him from contact with Barton. She had not even mentioned Barton to Arthur because—because—well, because Arthur was so much better, and somehow (she admitted it to herself now) she had not been sure that Arthur would care for her long, if at all, and then—well, and then, to be quite frank, Barton might be good enough. She did not exactly hate him because she had found Arthur—not at all. She still liked him in a way—he was so kind and faithful, so very dull and straightforward and thoughtful of her, which Arthur was certainly not. Before Arthur had appeared, as she well remembered, Barton had seemed to be plenty good enough—in fact, all that she desired in a pleasant, companionable way, calling for her, taking her places, bringing her flowers and candy, which Arthur rarely did, and for that, if nothing more, she could not help continuing to like him and to feel sorry for him, and, besides, as she had admitted to herself before, if Arthur left her—. . . Weren't his parents better off than hers—and hadn't he a good position for such a man as he—one hundred and fifty dollars a month and the certainty of more later on? A little while before meeting Arthur, she had thought this very good, enough for two to live on at least, and she had thought some of trying it at some time or other—but now—now—

And that first night he had called—how well she remembered it—how it had transfigured the parlor next this in which she was now, filling it with something it had never had before, and the porch outside, too, for that matter, with its gaunt, leafless vine, and this street, too, even—dull, commonplace Bethune Street. There had been a flurry of snow during the afternoon while she was working at the store, and the ground was white with it. All the neighboring homes seemed to look sweeter and happier and more inviting than ever they had as she came past them, with their lights peeping from under curtains and drawn shades. She had hurried into hers and lighted the big red-shaded parlor lamp, her one artistic treasure, as she thought, and put it near the piano, between it and the window, and arranged the chairs, and then bustled to the task of making herself as pleasing as she might. For him she had gotten out her one best filmy house dress and done up her hair in the fashion she thought most becoming—and that he had not seen before—and powdered her cheeks and nose and darkened her eyelashes, as some of the girls at the store did, and put on her new gray satin slippers, and then, being so arrayed, waited nervously, unable to eat anything or to think of anything but him.

And at last, just when she had begun to think he might not be coming, he had appeared with that arch smile and a "Hello! It's here you live, is it? I was wondering. George, but you're twice as sweet as I thought you were, aren't you?" And then, in the little entryway, behind the closed door, he had held her and kissed her on the mouth a dozen times while she pretended to push against his coat and struggle and say that her parents might hear.

And, oh, the room afterward, with him in it in the red glow of the lamp, and with his pale handsome face made handsomer thereby, as she thought! He had made her sit near him and had held her hands and told her about his work and his dreams—all that he expected to do in the future—and then she had found herself wishing intensely to share just such a life—his life—anything that he might wish to do; only, she kept wondering, with a slight pain, whether he would want her to—he was so young, dreamful, ambitious, much younger and more dreamful than herself, although, in reality, he was several years older.

And then followed that glorious period from December to this late September, in which everything which was worth happening in love had happened. Oh, those wondrous days, the following spring, when, with the first burst of buds and leaves, he had taken her one Sunday to Atholby, where all the great woods were, and they had hunted spring beauties in the grass, and sat on a slope and looked at the river below and watched some boys fixing up a sailboat and setting forth in it quite as she wished she and Arthur might be doing—going somewhere together—far, far away from all commonplace things and life! And then he had slipped his arm about her and kissed her cheek and neck, and tweaked her ear and smoothed her hair—and oh, there on the grass, with the spring flowers about her and a canopy of small green leaves above, the perfection of love had come—love so wonderful that the mere thought of it made her eyes brim now! And then had been days, Saturday afternoons and Sundays, at Atholby and Sparrows Point, where the great beach was, and in lovely Tregore Park, a mile or two from her home, where they could go of an evening and sit in or near the pavilion and have ice cream and dance or watch the dancers. Oh, the stars, the winds, the summer breath of those days! Ah, me! Ah, me!

Naturally, her parents had wondered from the first about her and Arthur, and her and Barton, since Barton had already assumed a proprietary interest in her and she had seemed to like him. But then she was an only child and a pet, and used to presuming on that, and they could not think of saying anything to her. After all, she was young and pretty and was entitled to change her mind; only, only— she had had to indulge in a career of lying and subterfuge in connection with Barton, since Arthur was head-strong and wanted every evening that he chose—to call for her at the store and keep her downtown to dinner and a show.

Arthur had never been like Barton, shy, phlegmatic, obedient, waiting long and patiently for each little favor, but, instead, masterful and eager, rifling her of kisses and caresses and every delight of love, and teasing and playing with her as a cat would a mouse. She could never resist him. He demanded of her her time and her affection without let or hindrance. He was not exactly selfish or cruel, as some might have been, but gay and unthinking at times, unconsciously so, and yet loving and tender at others—nearly always so. But always he would talk of things in the future as if they really did not include her—and this troubled her greatly—of places he might go, things he might do, which, somehow, he seemed to think or assume that she could not or would not do with him. He was always going to Australia sometime, he thought, in a business way, or to South Africa, or possibly to India. He never seemed to have any fixed clear future for himself in mind.

A dreadful sense of helplessness and of impending disaster came over her at these times, of being involved in some predicament over which she had no control, and which would lead her on to some sad end. Arthur, although plainly in love, as she thought, and apparently delighted with her, might not always love her. She began, timidly at first (and always, for that matter), to ask him pretty, seeking questions about himself and her, whether their future was certain to be together, whether he really wanted her—loved her—whether he might not want to marry someone else or just her, and whether she wouldn't look nice in a pearl satin wedding dress with a long creamy veil and satin slippers and a bouquet of bridalwreath. She had been so slowly but surely saving to that end, even before he came, in connection with Barton; only, after *he* came, all thought of the import of it had been transferred to him. But now, also, she was beginning to ask herself sadly, "Would it ever be?" He was so airy, so inconsequential, so ready to say: "Yes, yes," and "Sure, sure! that's right! Yes, indeedy, you bet! Say, kiddie, but you'll look sweet!" but, somehow, it had always seemed as if this whole thing were a glorious interlude and that it could not last. Arthur was too gay and ethereal and too little settled in his own mind. His ideas of travel and living in different cities, finally winding up in New York or San Francisco, but never with her exactly until she asked him, were too ominous, although he always reassured her gaily: "Of course! Of course!" But somehow she could never believe it really, and it made her intensely sad at times, horribly gloomy. So often she wanted to cry, and she could scarcely tell why.

And then, because of her affection for him, she had finally quarreled with Barton, or nearly that, if one could say that one ever really quarreled with him. It had been because of a certain Thursday evening a few weeks before about which she had disappointed him. In a fit of generosity, knowing that Arthur was coming Wednesday, and because Barton had stopped in at the store to see her, she had told him that he might come, having regretted it afterwards, so enamored was she of Arthur. And then when Wednesday came, Arthur had changed his mind, telling her he would come Friday instead, but on Thursday evening he had stopped in at the store and asked her to go to Sparrows Point, with the result that she had no time to notify Barton. He had gone to the house and sat with her parents until ten-thirty, and then, a few days later, although she had written him offering an excuse, had called at the store to complain slightly.

"Do you think you did just right, Shirley? You might have sent word, mightn't you? Who was it—the new fellow you won't tell me about?"

Shirley flared on the instant.

"Supposing it was? What's it to you? I don't belong to you yet, do I? I told you there wasn't any one, and I wish you'd let me alone about that. I couldn't help it last Thursday —that's all—and I don't want you to be fussing with me— that's all. If you don't want to, you needn't come any more, anyhow."

"Don't say that, Shirley," pleaded Barton. "You don't mean that. I won't bother you, though, if you don't want me any more."

And because Shirley sulked, not knowing what else to do, he had gone and she had not seen him since.

And then sometime later when she had thus broken with Barton, avoiding the railway station where he worked, Arthur had failed to come at his appointed time, sending no word until the next day, when a note came to the store saying that he had been out of town for his firm over Sunday and had not been able to notify her, but that he would call Tuesday. It was an awful blow. At the time, Shirley had a vision of what was to follow. It seemed for the moment as if the whole world had suddenly been reduced to ashes, that there was nothing but black charred cinders anywhere—she felt that about all life. Yet it all came to her clearly then that this was but the beginning of just such days and just such excuses, and that soon, soon, he would come no more. He was beginning to be tired of her and soon he would not even make excuses. She felt it, and it froze and terrified her.

And then, soon after, the indifference which she feared did follow—almost created by her own thoughts, as it were. First, it was a meeting he had to attend somewhere one Wednesday night when he was to have come for her. Then he was going out of town again, over Sunday. Then he was going away for a whole week—it was absolutely unavoidable, he said, his commercial duties were increasing—and once he had casually remarked that nothing could stand in the way where she was concerned—never! She did not think of reproaching him with this; she was too proud. If he was going, he must go. She would not be willing to say to herself that she had ever attempted to hold any man. But, just the same, she was agonized by the thought. When he was with her, he seemed tender enough; only, at times, his eyes wandered and he seemed slightly bored. Other girls, particularly pretty ones, seemed to interest him as much as she did.

And the agony of the long days when he did not come any more for a week or two at a time! The waiting, the brooding, the wondering, at the store and here in her home—in the former place making mistakes at times because she could not get her mind off him and being reminded of them, and here at her own home at nights, being so absent-minded that her parents remarked on it. She felt sure that her parents must be noticing that Arthur was not coming any more, or as much as he had—for she pretended to be going out with him, going to Mabel Gove's instead—and that Barton had deserted her too, he having been driven off by her indifference, never to come any more, perhaps, unless she sought him out.

And then it was that the thought of saving her own face by taking up with Barton once more occurred to her, of using him and his affections and faithfulness and dullness, if you will, to cover up her own dilemma. Only, this ruse was not to be tried until she had written Arthur this one letter—

a pretext merely to see if there was a single ray of hope, a letter to be written in a gentle-enough way and asking for the return of the few notes she had written him. She had not seen him now in nearly a month, and the last time she had, he had said he might soon be compelled to leave her awhile—to go to Pittsburgh to work. And it was his reply to this that she now held in her hand—from Pittsburgh! It was frightful! The future without him!

But Barton would never know really what had transpired, if she went back to him. In spite of all her delicious hours with Arthur, she could call him back, she felt sure. She had never really entirely dropped him, and he knew it. He had bored her dreadfully on occasion, arriving on off days when Arthur was not about, with flowers or candy, or both, and sitting on the porch steps and talking of the railroad business and of the whereabouts and doings of some of their old friends. It was shameful, she had thought at times, to see a man so patient, so hopeful, so good-natured as Barton, deceived in this way, and by her, who was so miserable over another. Her parents must see and know, she had thought at these times, but still, what else was she to do?

"I'm a bad girl," she kept telling herself. "I'm all wrong. What right have I to offer Barton what is left?" But still, somehow, she realized that Barton, if she chose to favor him, would only be too grateful for even the leavings of others where she was concerned, and that even yet, if she but deigned to crook a finger, she could have him. He was so simple, so good-natured, so stolid and matter of fact, so different to Arthur whom (she should not help smiling at the thought of it) she was loving now about as Barton loved her —slavishly, hopelessly.

And then, as the days passed and Arthur did not write

any more—just this one brief note—she at first grieved horribly, and then in a fit of numb despair attempted, bravely enough from one point of view, to adjust herself to the new situation. Why should she despair? Why die of agony where there were plenty who would still sigh for her—Barton among others? She was young, pretty, very—many told her so. She could, if she chose, achieve a vivacity which she did not feel. Why should she brook this unkindness without a thought of retaliation? Why shouldn't she enter upon a gay and heartless career, indulging in a dozen flirtations at once—dancing and killing all thoughts of Arthur in a round of frivolities? There were many who beckoned to her. She stood at the counter in the drugstore on many a day and brooded over this, but at the thought of which one to begin with, she faltered. After her late love, all were so tame, for the present anyhow.

And then—and then—always there was Barton, the humble or faithful, to whom she had been so unkind and whom she had used and whom she still really liked. So often self-reproaching thoughts in connection with him crept over her. He must have known, must have seen how badly she was using him all this while, and yet he had not failed to come and come, until she had actually quarreled with him, and any one would have seen that it was literally hopeless. She could not help remembering, especially now in her pain, that he adored her. He was not calling on her now at all—by her indifference she had finally driven him away—but a word, a word—she waited for days, weeks, hoping against hope, and then—

The office of Barton's superior in the Great Eastern terminal had always made him an easy object for her blandishments, coming and going, as she frequently did via this very station. He was in the office of the assistant train-despatcher on the ground floor, where passing to and from the local, which, at times, was quicker than a streetcar, she could easily see him by peering in; only, she had carefully avoided him for nearly a year. If she chose now, and would call for a message blank at the adjacent telegraph window which was a part of his room, and raised her voice as she often had in the past, he could scarcely fail to hear, if he did not see her. And if he did, he would rise and come over—of that she was sure, for he never could resist her. It had been a wile of hers in the old days to do this or to make her presence felt by idling outside. After a month of brooding, she felt that she must act—her position as a deserted girl was too much. She could not stand it any longer really—the eyes of her mother, for one.

It was six-fifteen one evening when, coming out of the store in which she worked, she turned her step disconsolately homeward. Her heart was heavy, her face rather pale and drawn. She had stopped in the store's retiring room before coming out to add to her charms as much as possible by a little powder and rouge and to smooth her hair. It would not take much to reallure her former sweetheart, she felt sure— and yet it might not be so easy after all. Suppose he had found another? But she could not believe that. It had scarcely been long enough since he had last attempted to see her, and he was really so very, very fond of her and so faithful. He was too slow and certain in his choosing—he had been so with her. Still, who knows? With this thought, she went forward in the evening, feeling for the first time the shame and pain that comes of deception, the agony of having to re-linquish an ideal and the feeling of despair that comes to those who find themselves in the position of suppliants, stooping to something which in better days and better fortune they would not know. Arthur was the cause of this.

When she reached the station, the crowd that usually filled it at this hour was swarming. There were so many pairs like Arthur and herself laughing and hurrying away or so she felt. First glancing in the small mirror of a weighing scale to see if she were still of her former charm, she stopped thoughtfully at a little flower stand which stood outside, and for a few pennies purchased a tiny bunch of violets. She then went inside and stood near the window, peering first furtively to see if he were present. He was. Bent over his work, a green shade over his eyes, she could see his solid genial figure at a table. Stepping back a moment to ponder, she finally went forward and, in a clear voice asked.

"May I have a blank, please?"

The infatuation of the discarded Barton was such that it brought him instantly to his feet. In his stodgy, stocky way he rose, his eyes glowing with a friendly hope, his mouth wreathed in smiles, and came over. At the sight of her, pale, but pretty—paler and prettier, really, than he had ever seen her—he thrilled dumbly.

"How are you, Shirley?" he asked sweetly, as he drew near, his eyes searching her face hopefully. He had not seen her for so long that he was intensely hungry, and her paler beauty appealed to him more than ever. Why wouldn't she have him? he was asking himself. Why wouldn't his persistent love yet win her? Perhaps it might. "I haven't seen you in a month of Sundays, it seems. How are the folks?"

"They're all right, Bart," she smiled archly, "and so am I. How have you been? It has been a long time since I've seen you. I've been wondering how you were. Have you been all right? I was just going to send a message."

As he had approached, Shirley had pretended at first not to see him, a moment later to affect surprise, although she was really suppressing a heavy sigh. The sight of him, after Arthur, was not reassuring. Could she really interest herself in him any more? Could she?

"Sure, sure," he replied genially; "I'm always all right. You couldn't kill me, you know. Not going away, are you, Shirl?" he queried interestedly.

"No; I'm just telegraphing to Mabel. She promised to meet me tomorrow, and I want to be sure she will."

"You don't come past here as often as you did, Shirley," he complained tenderly. "At least, I don't seem to see you so often," he added with a smile. "It isn't anything I have done, is it?" he queried, and then, when she protested quickly, added: "What's the trouble, Shirl? Haven't been sick, have you?"

She affected all her old gaiety and ease, feeling as though she would like to cry.

"Oh, no," she returned; "I've been all right. I've been going through the other door, I suppose, or coming in and going out on the Langdon Avenue car." (This was true, because she had been wanting to avoid him.) "I've been in such a hurry, most nights, that I haven't had time to stop, Bart. You know how late the store keeps us at times."

He remembered, too, that in the old days she had made time to stop or meet him occasionally.

"Yes, I know," he said tactfully. "But you haven't been to any of our old card parties either of late, have you? At least, I haven't seen you. I've come to two or three, thinking you might be there."

That was another thing Arthur had done—broken up her interest in these old store and neighborhood parties and a banjo-and-mandolin club to which she had once belonged. They had all seemed so pleasing and amusing in the old days —but now. . . . In those days Bart had been her usual companion when his work permitted.

"No," she replied evasively, but with a forced air of pleasant remembrance;" I have often thought of how much fun we had at those, though. It was a shame to drop them. You haven't seen Harry Stull or Trina Trask recently, have you?" she inquired, more to be saying something than for any interest she felt.

He shook his head negatively, then added:

"Yes, I did, too; here in the waiting room a few nights ago. They were coming downtown to a theater, I suppose."

His face fell slightly as he recalled how it had been their custom to do this, and what their one quarrel had been about. Shirley noticed it. She felt the least bit sorry for him, but much more for herself, coming back so disconsolately to all this.

"Well, you're looking as pretty as ever, Shirley," he continued, noting that she had not written the telegram and that there was something wistful in her glance. "Prettier, I think," and she smiled sadly. Every word that she tolerated from him was as so much gold to him, so much of dead ashes to her. "You wouldn't like to come down some evening this week and see 'The Mouse-Trap,' would you? We haven't been to a theater together in I don't know when." His eyes sought hers in a hopeful, doglike way.

So—she could have him again—that was the pity of it! To have what she really did not want, did not care for! At the least nod now he would come, and this very devotion made it all but worthless, and so sad. She ought to marry him now for certain, if she began in this way, and could in a month's time if she chose, but oh, oh—could she? For the moment she decided that she could not, would not. If he had only repulsed her—told her to go—ignored her—but no; it was her fate to be loved by him in this moving, pleading way, and hers not to love him as she wished to love—to be loved. Plainly, he needed some one like her, whereas she, she—She turned a little sick, a sense of the sacrilege of gaiety at this time creeping into her voice, and exclaimed:

"No, no!" Then seeing his face change, a heavy sadness come over it, "Not this week, anyhow, I mean" ("Not so soon," she had almost said). "I have several engagements this week and I'm not feeling well. But"—seeing his face change, and the thought of her own state returning—"you might come out to the house some evening instead, and then we can go some other time."

His face brightened intensely. It was wonderful how he longed to be with her, how the least favor from her comforted and lifted him up. She could see also now, however, how little it meant to her, how little it could ever mean, even if to him it was heaven. The old relationship would have to be resumed in toto, once and for all, but did she want it that way now that she was feeling so miserable about this other affair? As she meditated, these various moods racing to and fro in her mind, Barton seemed to notice, and now it occurred to him that perhaps he had not pursued her enough—was too easily put off. She probably did like him yet. This evening, her present visit, seemed to prove it.

"Sure, sure!" he agreed. "I'd like that. I'll come out Sunday, if you say. We can go any time to the play. I'm sorry, Shirley, if you're not feeling well. I've thought of you a lot these days. I'll come out Wednesday, if you don't mind."

She smiled a wan smile. It was all so much easier than

she had expected—her triumph—and so ashenlike in consequence, a flavor of dead-sea fruit and defeat about it all, that it was pathetic. How could she, after Arthur? How could he, really?

"Make it Sunday," she pleaded, naming the farthest day off, and then hurried out.

Her faithful lover gazed after her, while she suffered an intense nausea. To think—to think—it should all be coming to this! She had not used her telegraph blank, and now had forgotten all about it. It was not the simple trickery that discouraged her, but her own future which could find no better outlet than this, could not rise above it apparently, or that she had no heart to make it rise above it. Why couldn't she interest herself in some one different to Barton? Why did she have to return to him? Why not wait and meet some other—ignore him as before? But no, no; nothing mattered now—no one—it might as well be Barton as any one, and she would at least make him happy and at the same time solve her own problem. She went out into the train shed and climbed into her train. Slowly, after the usual pushing and jostling of a crowd, it drew out toward Latonia, that suburban region in which her home lay. As she rode, she thought.

"What have I just done? What am I doing?" she kept asking herself as the clacking wheels on the rails fell into a rhythmic dance and the houses of the brown, dry, endless city fled past in a maze. "Severing myself decisively from the past—the happy past—for supposing, once I am married, Arthur should return and want me again—suppose! Suppose!"

Below at one place, under a shed, were some market gardeners disposing of the last remnants of their day's wares

—a sickly, dull life, she thought. Here was Rutgers Avenue, with its line of red streetcars, many wagons and tracks and counterstreams of automobiles—how often had she passed it morning and evening in a shuttle-like way, and how often would, unless she got married! And here, now, was the river flowing smoothly between its banks lined with coal pockets and wharves—away, away to the huge deep sea which she and Arthur had enjoyed so much. Oh, to be in a small boat and drift out, out into the endless, restless, pathless deep! Somehow the sight of this water, tonight and every night, brought back those evenings in the open with Arthur at Sparrows Point, the long line of dancers in Eckert's Pavilion, the woods at Atholby, the park, with the dancers in the pavilion—she choked back a sob. Once Arthur had come this way with her on just such an evening as this, pressing her hand and saying how wonderful she was. Oh, Arthur! Arthur! And now Barton was to take his old place again— forever, no doubt. She could not trifle with her life longer in this foolish way, or his. What was the use? But think of it!

Yes, it must be—forever now, she told herself. She must marry. Time would be slipping by and she would become too old. It was her only future—marriage. It was the only future she had ever contemplated really, a home, children, the love of some man whom she could love as she loved Arthur. Ah, what a happy home that would have been for her! But now, now—

But there must be no turning back now, either. There was no other way. If Arthur ever came back—but fear not, he wouldn't! She had risked so much and lost—lost him. Her little venture into true love had been such a failure. Before Arthur had come all had been well enough. Barton, stout and simple and frank and direct, had in some way—how, she could scarcely realize now—offered sufficient of a future. But now, now! He had enough money, she knew, to build a cottage for the two of them. He had told her so. He would do his best always to make her happy, she was sure of that. They could live in about the state her parents were living in—or a little better, not much—and would never want. No doubt there would be children, because he craved them—several of them—and that would take up her time, long years of it—the sad, gray years! But then Arthur, whose children she would have thrilled to bear, would be no more, a mere memory—think of that!—and Barton, the dull, the commonplace, would have achieved his finest dream—and why?

Because love was a failure for her—that was why—and in her life there would be no more true love. She would never love any one again as she had Arthur. It could not be, she was sure of it. He was too fascinating, too wonderful. Always, always, wherever she might be, whoever she might marry, he would be coming back, intruding between her and any possible love, receiving any possible kiss. It would be Arthur she would be loving or kissing. She dabbed at her eyes with a tiny handkerchief, turned her face close to the window and stared out, and then as the environs of Latonia came into view, wondered (so deep is romance): What if Arthur should come back at some time—or now! Supposing he should be here at the station now, accidentally or on purpose, to welcome her, to soothe her weary heart. He had met her here before. How she would fly to him, lay her head on his shoulder, forget forever that Barton ever was, that they had ever separated for an hour. Oh, Arthur! Arthur!

But no, no; here was Latonia—here the viaduct over her train, the long business street and the cars marked "Center" and "Langdon Avenue" running back into the great city.

A few blocks away in tree-shaded Bethune Street, duller and plainer than ever, was her parents' cottage and the routine of that old life which was now, she felt, more fully fastened upon her than ever before—the lawn mowers, the lawns, the front porches all alike. Now would come the going to and fro of Barton to business as her father and she now went to business, her keeping house, cooking, washing, ironing, sewing for Barton as her mother now did these things for her father and herself. And she would not be in love really, as she wanted to be. Oh, dreadful! She could never escape it really, now that she could endure it less, scarcely for another hour. And yet she must, must, for the sake of—for the sake of—she closed her eyes and dreamed.

She walked up the street under the trees, past the houses and lawns all alike to her own, and found her father on their veranda reading the evening paper. She sighed at the sight.

"Back, daughter?" he called pleasantly.

"Yes."

"Your mother is wondering if you would like steak or liver for dinner. Better tell her."

"Oh, it doesn't matter."

She hurried into her bedroom, threw down her hat and gloves, and herself on the bed to rest silently, and groaned in her soul. To think that it had all come to this!—Never to see him any more!—To see only Barton, and marry him and live in such a street, have four or five children, forget all her youthful companionships—and all to save her face before her parents, and her future. Why must it be? Should it be, really? She choked and stifled. After a little time her mother, hearing her come in, came to the door—thin, practical, affectionate, conventional.

"What's wrong, honey? Aren't you feeling well to-night? Have you a headache? Let me feel."

Her thin cool fingers crept over her temples and hair. She suggested something to eat or a headache powder right away.

"I'm all right, mother. I'm just not feeling well now. Don't bother. I'll get up soon. Please don't."

"Would you rather have liver or steak tonight, dear?"

"Oh, anything—nothing—please don't bother—steak will do—anything"—if only she could get rid of her and be at rest.

Her mother looked at her and shook her head sympathetically, then retreated quietly, saying no more. Lying so, she thought and thought—grinding, destroying thoughts about the beauty of the past, the darkness of the future—until able to endure them no longer she got up and, looking distractedly out of the window into the yard and the house next door, stared at her future fixedly. What should she do? What should she really do? There was Mrs. Kessel in her kitchen getting her dinner as usual, just as her own mother was now, and Mr. Kessel out on the front porch in his shirt sleeves reading the evening paper. Beyond was Mr. Pollard in his yard, cutting the grass. All along Bethune Street were such houses and such people—simple, commonplace souls all —clerks, managers, fairly successful craftsmen, like her father and Barton, excellent in their way but not like Arthur the beloved, the lost—and here was she, perforce, or by decision of necessity, soon to be one of them, in some such street as this no doubt, forever and—. For the moment it choked and stifled her.

She decided that she would not. No, no, no! There must be some other way—many ways. She did not have to do this unless she really wished to—would not—only—. Then going to the mirror she looked at her face and smoothed her hair.

"But what's the use?" she asked of herself wearily and resignedly after a time. "Why should I cry? Why shouldn't I marry Barton? I don't amount to anything, anyhow. Arthur wouldn't have me. I wanted him, and I am compelled to take some one else—or no one—what difference does it really make who? My dreams are too high, that's all. I wanted Arthur, and he wouldn't have me. I don't want Barton, and he crawls at my feet. I'm a failure. that's what's the matter with me."

And then, turning up her sleeves and removing a fichu which stood out too prominently from her breast, she went into the kitchen and, looking about for an apron, observed:

"Can't I help? Where's the tablecloth?" and finding it among napkins and silverware in a drawer in the adjoining room, proceeded to set the table.

FICTION: GENERAL QUESTIONS

1. From the reader's viewpoint a work of literature is successful because it "reaches" him, providing him with an experience. Which piece of fiction "reached" you? Why? Which failed to impress you?

2. Does any one selection strike you as timeless and enduring? What are the particular elements or qualities that make you feel and think this work would be effective with different people in a different place and at another time?

3. Do you identify with a given character more than any other? For what reasons?

4. Which writer most impressed you with his technique, style and use of language?

5. What ideas were best represented in which story?

6. Is one author outstanding in the development of character portraits—in making the people come alive on the printed page?

7. Which story best represents the mood of the twenties? the attitudes of the people of the period?

8. It has been said the purpose of literature is to teach and to entertain. Which work of fiction fulfills this purpose?

9. A critic has stated that the justification of literature is that it presents us with a picture or impression of life, an interest in what people think and feel, and why they act. Apply this statement to a particular selection.

10. In addition to their emotional impact, many stories are instruments to think with. Which piece of fiction provided you with a significant intellectual experience?

11. Did any selection impress you with a sense of the importance of the things it depicted?

Cather:

Is Paul doomed because of society and his immediate environment?

Was his problem insoluble?

What is the meaning of Paul's quest for beauty?

Does he represent sensitive young people today?

How does Cather use symbols?

How is the author's sympathy for Paul revealed?

Tarkington:

> Why is this a tragic story?
> What are Alice's shortcomings?
> To what extent do you identify with her?
> Is the story plausible? Why?
> Is the story "dated"?
> What are the similarities with "Paul's Case"?

Hemingway:

> How would you explain Harold's attitude toward life?
> How has the war influenced him?
> Does the story appear to be "real"?
> Is Hemingway's feeling of disillusionment evident?
> How would you compare Harold and his family with the heroine and family in *Alice Adams*?
> Are there any resemblances between Harold and the hero of "Paul's Case?"

Parker:

> Are you sympathetic toward the narrator?
> In what ways do the author's ironic views appear in this selection?
> Compare the central figure with the heroine of *Alice Adams*.

Fitzgerald:

> Why have Dexter's dreams disappeared?
> Can you identify with his attitudes?
> How would you compare Dexter with the hero in Hemingway's "Soldier's Home"?
> As the fictional spokesman for the twenties, how is Fitzgerald's point of view reflected in this story?

Wolfe:

Wolfe created many poetic passages in his novels. Identify the poetry in this selection.

What does the author mean by "other kinds" of death?

Why does Eugene say he will never return?

Anderson:

How does the author portray the tragic existence of the story's central character?

Is Wing a "grotesque"?

What is Anderson's method of handling dialogue?

What passages show the author's views on small-town life?

Lardner:

What is the nature of Lardner's humor?

What techniques are used by the author to probe human behavior?

What are your feelings about practical jokes?

Are there any similarities between the people in this story and those in Anderson's "Hands"?

Dell:

What is the impact of this short story?

What does Dell say about old age and the difference between generations?

What is the real tragedy in this tale?

Lewis:

How does the author deal with conformity and standardization?

What is your estimate of Mr. Babbitt? of Mrs. Babbitt?
Are they "real" people or stereotypes?
What are the satirical elements in this selection?
Does Lewis show compassion for his people?

Dreiser:

Is Shirley a failure? Why?
Does she resemble the heroine in *Alice Adams*?
Is she really making a "second choice"?
Why is this a naturalistic story?

1. Beauty contest
   at Atlantic City, New Jersey, September 1924.

2.   Ad in *Vogue* magazine, August 15, 1926,
     showing women's fashions in the Twenties.

3.
Clara Bow,
the original "It" girl,
Sex Symbol of the
Jazz Age in the movies.

4. Harold Lloyd in one of his hit movie comedies of the 1920's.

5.
Charlie Chaplin *(l.)* and
Jackie Coogan in *The Kid*,
a classic movie of the period.

6.
Al Jolson,
with supporting actress,
in *The Jazz Singer*, the first
"all-talking" motion picture.

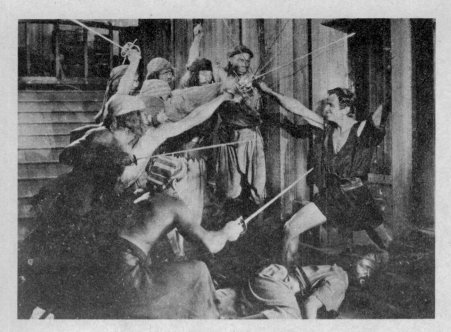

7.
Douglas Fairbanks *(r.)*,
screen swashbuckler,
crosses swords
in *The Black Pirate*,
a 1926 movie.

8.
Rudolph Valentino,
the "Great Lover" of the
movies in the Twenties.

9. Mary Pickford,
   "America's Sweetheart" of the movies in the Jazz Age.

10. Charles A. Lindbergh shown with his plane, "The Spirit of St. Louis," in which he flew solo across the Atlantic Ocean to Paris in May 1927.

11. George Herman ("Babe") Ruth, the home-run king, of the N. Y. Yankees baseball team.

12. "Big Bill" Tilden, tennis champion in the Twenties, another of the stars of "The Golden Age" in American sports.

13.
Jack Dempsey (*l.*) in heavy-
weight bout with Tom
Gibbons in Shelby, Montana,
July 4, 1923.

14.
Bobby Jones,
U.S. Open Golf Champion,
in 1926. Note the "plus
fours" or "knickers"
(trousers) he wore, the usual
golf outfit at that time.

15.   Red Grange, the "Galloping Ghost," one of the great
college (U. of Illinois) football players of the 1920's.

16.   Graham MacNamee (r.), a famous radio announcer,
and the Cliquot Club Eskimos orchestra.

17–18.   Two popular songs of The Jazz Age.
"Makin' Whoopee" was introduced by Eddie Cantor,
star entertainer, in the Ziegfeld musical comedy "Whoopee."

19. Paul Whiteman, "The King of Jazz," and his orchestra at the Palais D'Or night club in the 1920's.

20.
An early radio set, with separate speaker, and powered by batteries.

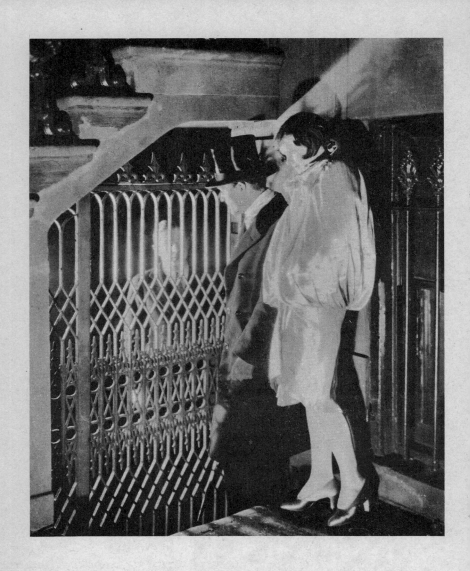

21. Entrance to a "speakeasy,"
an illegal saloon during the Prohibition Era.

WINES

Williams & Humberts
  Port & Sherry .... $2.00 qt. $22.00
Diamond Jubilee Port, Sherry .... 2.50 qt. 25.00
B & G Sauterne .... 2.50 qt. 25.00
Champagne
  $7.50 qt. 2 for $14.00
All other Wines can be obtained upon request

CORDIALS

The following brands are always on hand:
  Marie Brizard   P. Garnier
      Fremy Fil's (Fruit Cordials)
These three brands are always at hand in the
following flavors:
  Creme de Menthe   Mandarin
  Creme de Cacao   Blackberry
  Apricot   Cerise
            Especially priced at $3.00 qt.
Cointreau   Benedictine   Chartreuse
            Especially priced at $4.00 qt.

C O G N A C

Hennessey***   ⎫   Specially
Martel   ⎬   priced
Bisquit Dubouche ⎭   at $4.00 the qt.
190 Proof Government Tested Grain
Alcohol   Qt. $2.00 Gal. $6.00

JUST PHONE

NELSON

All merchandise may be sampled
before you pay.

We Deliver Anywhere - Promptly.

BEekman 3-3430

22.
Advertising circular
and price list
for liquor
during prohibition.

23.
A famous Rollin Kirby
cartoon, from
the *New York World*,
July 25, 1921, showing
"rum runners' row"
just outside the
"Three Mile Limit"
of the Volstead Act.

24. Four gangsters of the Prohibition Era,
with Charles ("Lucky") Luciano on the far right of the
picture.

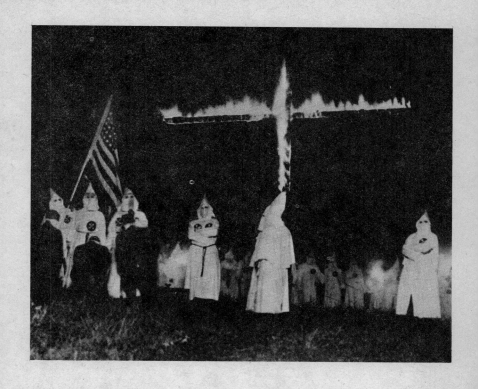

25. A Ku Klux Klan gathering and cross-burning just across
the Potomac River from Washington, D.C., in April 1924.

26.
Cartoon,
drawn by Fish,
in the November
1926 issue of a
popular magazine
of "The Roaring
Twenties."

The Best Comedy in America

College Humor

LUCIAN CARY
ROYAL BROWN
JOHN V. A. WEAVER
ELLIS PARKER BUTLER
SCOTT FITZGERALD

Hearst's International
combined with
Cosmopolitan

January

35 Cents

All These
Ellen Glasgow
Irvin Cobb - Rex Beach
Fannie Hurst
Ring W. Lardner
A. S. M. Hutchinson
Theodore Roosevelt
Chas. G. Norris - George Ade
Ernest Poole - H. C. Witwer
James Oliver Curwood
W. Somerset Maugham
Sir Philip Gibbs and
The New Novel by the author of "Glorious Apollo"

27. Cover of *College Humor* magazine showing names of some
     well-known authors who appeared in that issue.

28. Note the distinguished authors listed on the cover
     of this issue of *Cosmopolitan Magazine* in the 1920's.

30.   The Sinclair Lewises (he wrote *Main Street, Babbitt, Arrowsmith,*
                              among other works) in their "Model T" Ford.

29.   Cover design for F. Scott Fitzgerald's
      Tales of the Jazz Age by John Held, Jr.,
      the artist whose drawings best satirized that period.

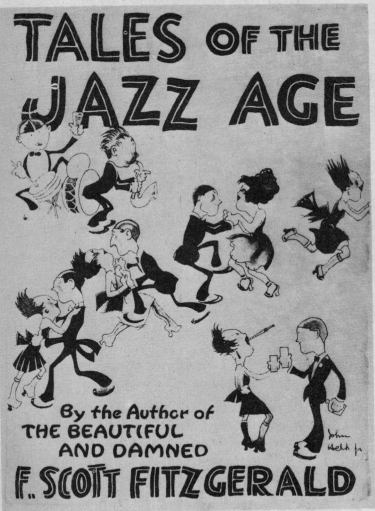

31.
F. Scott Fitzgerald, the novelist and short story writer whose writings epitomized the Jazz Age and whose novel, *The Great Gatsby*, became a modern classic, still read today.

34. H. L. (Henry Louis) Mencken, editor and social critic, coiner of the phrase, "booboisie," had an important influence on American writing in the 1920's.

33. Cover design for an early edition of *The Sun Also Rises*, one of Ernest Hemingway's most popular novels.

32. Ernest Hemingway as a young man in Paris in the 1920's when he was just beginning his literary career.

35.
Calvin Coolidge in Indian head-
dress after being made an
honorary Chief during one of his
political campaigns.

36.
President Woodrow Wilson in
San Diego on a speaking tour in
1919.

37.   President Coolidge *(c.)* and Herbert Hoover *(r.)*

38.   Warren G. Harding, 29th president of the United States.

39.   Schoolroom in Mendota Beach, Wisconsin, in 1922.

40.   Trolley cars
on State Street in Lafayette, Indiana, in 1928.

41.   Roadbuilding with two-ton tractor and scraper, in 1922.

42. View of one of the first supermarkets.

43.   Women's styles, and refrigerator, in the 1920's.

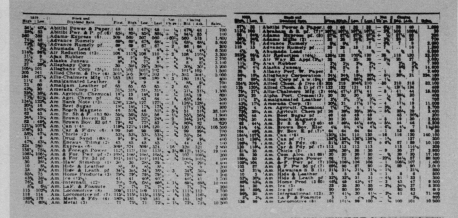

WORST STOCK CRASH STEMMED BY BANKS;
12,894,650-SHARE DAY SWAMPS MARKET;
LEADERS CONFER, FIND CONDITIONS SOUND

FINANCIERS EASE TENSION

Five Wall Street Bankers Hold Two Meetings at Morgan Office.

CALL BREAK 'TECHNICAL'

Wall Street Optimistic After Stormy Day; Clerical Work May Force Holiday Tomorrow

Confidence in the soundness of the stock market structure, notwithstanding the upheaval of the last few days, was voiced last night by bankers and other financial leaders. Sentiment as expressed by the heads of some of the largest banking institutions and by industrial executives as well was distinctly cheerful and the feeling was general that the worst had been seen. Wall Street ended the day in an optimistic frame of mind.

The opinion of brokers was unanimous that the selling had got out of hand not because of any inherent weakness in the market but because the public had become alarmed over the steady liquida-

LOSSES RECOVERED IN PART

Upward Trend Start With 200,000-Share Order for Steel.

TICKERS LAG FOUR HOURS

44. Stock market quotations and newspaper headlines of the 1929 stock market crash, the end of the Jazz Age and the beginning of "The Great Depression."

POETRY

Robert Frost (1874–1963)

Although born in San Francisco, Robert Frost spent most of his life in New England. He attended Dartmouth for a short time and then switched to Harvard where he earned his degree. During his lifetime he taught English at several colleges.

Frost's poetry won the Pulitzer Prize in 1924 and he received several Pultizers in the following decades. His poems, simple on the surface, describe New England people and places, but he constantly probes into the meaning of nature and human conduct. Creating conventional lyrics in blank verse, narratives, and dramatic monologues in varied moods ranging from tragic and satiric to comic, and using Yankee dialect, Frost succeeded in the unification of subject and language. Although Robert Frost's poems are regional in setting, they are universal in substance and significance.

ACQUAINTED WITH THE NIGHT

I have been one acquainted with the night.
I have walked out in rain—and back in rain.
I have outwalked the furthest city light.

I have looked down the saddest city lane.
I have passed by the watchman on his beat
And dropped my eyes, unwilling to explain.

I have stood still and stopped the sound of feet
When far away an interrupted cry
Came over houses from another street,

But not to call me back or say good-by;
And further still at an unearthly height,
One luminary clock against the sky

Proclaimed the time was neither wrong nor right.
I have been one acquainted with the night.

FIRE AND ICE

Some say the world will end in fire,
Some say in ice.
From what I've tasted of desire
I hold with those who favor fire.
But if it had to perish twice,
I think I know enough of hate
To say that for destruction ice
Is also great
And would suffice.

STOPPING BY WOODS
ON A SNOWY EVENING

Whose woods these are I think I know.
His house is in the village though;
He will not see me stopping here
To watch his woods fill up with snow.

My little horse must think it queer
To stop without a farmhouse near
Between the woods and frozen lake
The darkest evening of the year.

He gives his harness bells a shake
To ask if there is some mistake.
The only other sound's the sweep
Of easy wind and downy flake.

The woods are lovely, dark and deep,
But I have promises to keep,
And miles to go before I sleep,
And miles to go before I sleep.

ACCEPTANCE

When the spent sun throws up its rays on cloud
And goes down burning into the gulf below,
No voice in nature is heard to cry aloud
At what has happened. Birds, at least, must know
It is the change to darkness in the sky.
Murmuring something quiet in her breast,
One bird begins to close a faded eye;
Or overtaken too far from his nest,
Hurrying low above the grove, some waif
Swoops just in time to his remembered tree.
At most he thinks or twitters softly, "Safe!
Now let the night be dark for all of me.
Let the night be too dark for me to see
Into the future. Let what will be, be."

THE ONSET

Always the same, when on a fated night
At last the gathered snow lets down as white
As may be in dark woods, and with a song
It shall not make again all winter long
Of hissing on the yet uncovered ground,
I almost stumble looking up and round,
As one who overtaken by the end
Gives up his errand, and lets death descend
Upon him where he is, with nothing done
To evil, no important triumph won,
More than if life had never been begun.
Yet all the precedent is on my side:
I know that winter death has never tried
The earth but it has failed: the snow may heap
In long storms an undrifted four feet deep
As measured against maple, birch, and oak,
It cannot check the peeper's silver croak;
And I shall see the snow all go down hill
In water of a slender April rill
That flashes tail through last year's withered brake
And dead weeds, like a disappearing snake.
Nothing will be left white but here a birch,
And there a clump of houses with a church.

Countee Cullen (1902-1946)

A skillful lyricist in the tradition of the nineteenth-century romantic poets, Countee Cullen's major theme is the tragic life of the Negro in a white man's society. Born in New York City, educated in its public schools, a graduate of New York University and recipient of a master's degree from Harvard, he taught in the New York City schools. Countee Cullen's powerful lyrics express the pathos and plight of his people.

FROM THE DARK TOWER

We shall not always plant while others
   reap
The golden increment of bursting fruit,
Not always countenance, abject and mute,
That lesser men should hold their brothers
   cheap;
Not everlastingly while others sleep
Shall we beguile their limbs with mellow
   flute,

Not always bend to some more subtle brute;
We were not made eternally to weep.

The night whose sable breast relieves the
    stark,
White stars is no less lovely being dark,
And there are buds that cannot bloom at all
In light, but crumple, piteous, and fall;
So in the dark we hide the heart that bleeds,
And wait, and tend our agonizing seeds.

YET DO I MARVEL

I doubt not God is good, well-meaning, kind,
And did He stoop to quibble could tell why
The little buried mole continues blind,
Why flesh that mirrors Him must some day die,
Make plain the reason tortured Tantalus
Is baited by the fickle fruit, declare
If merely brute caprice dooms Sisyphus
To struggle up a never-ending stair.
Inscrutable His ways are, and immune
To catechism by a mind too strewn
With petty cares to slightly understand
What awful brain compels His awful hand.
Yet do I marvel at this curious thing:
To make a poet black, and bid him sing!

INCIDENT

Once riding in old Baltimore,
   Heart-filled, head-filled with glee,
I saw a Baltimorean
   Keep looking straight at me.

Now I was eight and very small,
   And he was no whit bigger,
And so I smiled, but he poked out
   His tongue, and called me, "Nigger."

I saw the whole of Baltimore
   From May until December;
Of all the things that happened there
   That's all that I remember.

Stephen Vincent Benét (1898–1943)

A graduate of Yale, Stephen Vincent Benét was born in Bethlehem, Pennsylvania. Idealism and a sense of affirmation mark his work. Although Benét wrote many short stories, novels and essays, he is best known for John Brown's Body, an epic poem in a variety of verse forms, which won the Pulitzer Prize in Poetry (1929). It was the most widely read long poem of the period. "Invocation" introduces this heroic and panoramic legend of the Civil War.

FROM JOHN BROWN'S BODY

INVOCATION

American muse, whose strong and diverse heart
So many men have tried to understand
But only made it smaller with their art,
Because you are as various as your land,

As mountainous-deep, as flowered with blue rivers,
Thirsty with deserts, buried under snows,
As native as the shape of Navajo quivers,
And native, too, as the sea-voyaged rose.

Swift runner, never captured or subdued,
Seven-branched elk beside the mountain stream,
That half a hundred hunters have pursued
But never matched their bullets with the dream,

Where the great huntsmen failed, I set my sorry
And mortal snare for your immortal quarry.

You are the buffalo ghost, the broncho-ghost
With dollar-silver in your saddle-horn,
The cowboys riding in from Painted Post,
The Indian arrow in the Indian corn,

And you are the clipped velvet of the lawns
Where Shropshire grows from Massachusetts' sods,
The grey Maine rocks—and the war-painted dawns
That break above the Garden of the Gods.

The prairie-schooners crawling toward the ore
And the cheap car, parked by the station-door.

Where the skyscrapers lift their foggy plumes
Of stranded smoke out of a stony mouth
You are that high stone and its arrogant fumes,
And you are ruined gardens in the South

And bleak New England farms, so winter-white
Even their roofs look lonely, and the deep
The middle grainland where the wind of night
Is like all blind earth sighing in her sleep.

A friend, an enemy, a sacred hag
With two tied oceans in her medicine-bag.

They tried to fit you with an English song
And clip your speech into the English tale.
But, even from the first, the words went wrong,
The catbird pecked away the nightingale.

The homesick men begot high-cheekboned things
Whose wit was whittled with a different sound
And Thames and all the rivers of the kings
Ran into Mississippi and were drowned.

They planted England with a stubborn trust.
But the cleft dust was never English dust.

Stepchild of every exile from content
And all the disavouched, hard-bitten pack
Shipped overseas to steal a continent
With neither shirts nor honor to their back.

Pimping grandee and rump-faced regicide,
Apple-cheeked younkers from a windmill-square,
Puritans stubborn as the nails of Pride,

Rakes from Versailles and thieves from County Clare,
The black-robed priests who broke their hearts in vain
To make you God and France or God and Spain.

These were your lovers in your buckskin-youth.
And each one married with a dream so proud
He never knew it could not be the truth
And that he coupled with a girl of cloud.

And now to see you is more difficult yet
Except as an immensity of wheel
Made up of wheels, oiled with inhuman sweat
And glittering with the heat of ladled steel.

All these you are, and each is partly you,
And none is false, and none is wholly true.

So how to see you as you really are,
So how to suck the pure, distillate, stored
Essence of essence from the hidden star
And make it pierce like a riposting sword.

For, as we hunt you down, you must escape
And we pursue a shadow of our own
That can be caught in a magician's cape
But has the flatness of a painted stone.

Never the running stag, the gull at wing,
The pure elixir, the American thing.

And yet, at moments when the mind was hot
With something fierier than joy or grief,
When each known spot was an eternal spot
And every leaf was an immortal leaf,

I think that I have seen you, not as one,
But clad in diverse semblances and powers,
Always the same, as light falls from the sun,
And always different, as the differing hours.

Yet, through each altered garment that you wore
The naked body, shaking the heart's core.

All day the snow fell on that Eastern town
With its soft, pelting, little, endless sigh
Of infinite flakes that brought the tall sky down
Till I could put my hands in the white sky

And taste cold scraps of heaven on my tongue
And walk in such a changed and luminous light
As gods inhabit when the gods are young.
All day it fell. And when the gathered night

Was a blue shadow cast by a pale glow
I saw you then, snow-image, bird of the snow.

And I have seen and heard you in the dry
Close-huddled furnace of the city street
When the parched moon was planted in the sky
And the limp air hung dead against the heat.

I saw you rise, red as that rusty plant,
Dizzied with lights, half-mad with senseless sound,
Enormous metal, shaking to the chant
Of a triphammer striking iron ground.

Enormous power, ugly to the fool,
And beautiful as a well-handled tool.

These, and the memory of that windy day
On the bare hills, beyond the last barbed wire,
When all the orange poppies bloomed one way
As if a breath would blow them into fire,

I keep forever, like the sea-lion's tusk
The broken sailor brings away to land,
But when he touches it, he smells the musk,
And the whole sea lies hollow in his hand.

So, from a hundred visions, I make one,
And out of darkness build my mocking sun.

And should that task seem fruitless in the eyes
Of those a different magic sets apart
To see through the ice-crystal of the wise
No nation but the nation that is Art,

Their words are just. But when the birchbark-call
Is shaken with the sound that hunters make
The moose comes plunging through the forest-wall
Although the rifle waits beside the lake.

Art has no nations—but the mortal sky
Lingers like gold in immortality.

This flesh was seeded from no foreign grain
But Pennsylvania and Kentucky wheat,
And it has soaked in California rain
And five years tempered in New England sleet

To strive at last, against an alien proof
And by the changes of an alien moon,
To build again that blue, American roof
Over a half-forgotten battle-tune

And call unsurely, from a haunted ground,
Armies of shadows and the shadow-sound.

In your Long House there is an attic-place
Full of dead epics and machines that rust,
And there, occasionally, with casual face,
You come awhile to stir the sleepy dust;

Neither in pride nor mercy, but in vast
Indifference at so many gifts unsought,
The yellowed satins, smelling of the past,
And all the loot the lucky pirates brought.

I only bring a cup of silver air,
Yet, in your casualness, receive it there.

Receive the dream too haughty for the breast,
Receive the words that should have walked as bold
As the storm walks along the mountaincrest
And are like beggars whining in the cold.

The maimed presumption, the unskilful skill,
The patchwork colors, fading from the first,
And all the fire that fretted at the will
With such a barren ecstasy of thirst.

Receive them all—and should you choose to touch them
With one slant ray of quick, American light,
Even the dust will have no power to smutch them,
Even the worst will glitter in the night.

If not—the dry bones littered by the way
May still point giants toward their golden prey.

James Weldon Johnson (1871–1938)

One of the foremost Negro writers, James Weldon Johnson was active in the struggle of the National Association for the Advancement of Colored People to improve the status of his people. In his poetry, essays, novels and biographical writings, Johnson pleads for Negro patience and greater educational opportunities. He was born in Jacksonville, Florida, and was graduated from Atlanta and Columbia universities. Johnson was a high school teacher and principal, and a professor at Fisk University. "The Creation" from God's Trombones depicts the oratory of old-time Negro preachers.

THE CREATION

And God stepped out on space
And he looked around and said:
"I'm lonely—
I'll make me a world."

And far as the eye of God could see,
Darkness covered everything,

Blacker than a hundred midnights
Down in a cypress swamp.

Then God smiled,
And the light broke,
And the darkness rolled up on one side,
And the light stood shining on the other,
And God said: "That's good!"

Then God reached out and took the light in his hands,
And God rolled the light around in his hands,
Until he made the sun;
And he set that sun a-blazing in the heavens.
And the light that was left from making the sun
God gathered it up in a shining ball
And flung it against the darkness,
Spangling the night with the moon and stars.
Then down between
The darkness and the light
He hurled the world;
And God said: "That's good!"

Then God himself stepped down—
And the sun was on his right hand,
And the moon was on his left;
The stars were clustered about his head,
And the earth was under his feet.
And God walked, and where he trod
His footsteps hollowed the valleys out
And bulged the mountains up.

Then he stopped and looked and saw
That earth was hot and barren.

So God stepped over to the edge of the world
And he spat out the seven seas;
He batted his eyes, and the lightnings flashed;
He clapped his hands, and the thunders rolled—
And the waters above the earth came down,
The cooling waters came down.

Then the green grass sprouted,
And the little red flowers blossomed,
The pine tree pointed his finger to the sky,
And the oak spread out his arms,
The lakes cuddled down in the hollows of the ground,
And the rivers ran down to the sea;
And God smiled again,
And the rainbow appeared,
And curled itself around his shoulder.

Then God raised his arm and he waved his hand
Over the sea and over the land,
And he said: "Bring forth! Bring forth!"
And quicker than God could drop his hand,
Fishes and fowls
And beasts and birds
Swam the rivers and the seas,
Roamed the forests and the woods,
And split the air with their wings.
And God said: "That's good!"

Then God walked around,
And God looked around
On all that he had made.

He looked at his sun,
And he looked at his moon,
And he looked at his little stars;
He looked on his world
With all its living things,
And God said: "I'm lonely still."

Then God sat down,
On the side of a hill where he could think;
By a deep, wide river he sat down,
With his head in his hands;
God thought and thought,
Till he thought: "I'll make me a man!"

Up from the bed of the river
God scooped the clay;
And by the bank of the river
He kneeled him down;
And there the great God Almighty—
Who lit the sun and fixed it in the sky,
Who flung the stars to the most far corner of the night,
Who rounded the earth in the middle of his hand—
This Great God,
Like a mammy bending over her baby,
Kneeled down in the dust,
Toiling over a lump of clay
Till he shaped it in his own image;

Then into it he blew the breath of life,
And man became a living soul.
Amen. Amen.

Edwin Arlington Robinson
(1869–1935)

One of the great poets of the era, awarded three Pulitzer Prizes in Poetry during the twenties, E. A. Robinson wrote traditional lyrics, sonnets and lengthy blank verse narratives to analyze the human condition. Using legends, the Bible and small-town life, his poems are psychological studies of man's struggle, analytical protraits of failures and the human flaws that cause their uncertainties and difficulties. Robinson's people are tragic, troubled and frustrated. Sardonic humor is one of his poetic weapons. Because much of his poetry is complex, the meanings are left to the reader's interpretation. E. A. Robinson was born in Head Tide, Maine, raised in Gardiner in the same state, and he attended Harvard.

GLASS HOUSES

Learn if you must, but do not come to me
For truth of what your pleasant neighbor says
Behind you of your looks or of your ways,
Or of your worth and virtue generally;

If he's a pleasure to you, let him be—
Being the same to him; and let your days
Be tranquil, having each the other's praise,
And each his own opinion peaceably.

Two others once did love each other well,
Yet not so well but that a pungent word
From each came stinging home to the wrong ears.
The rest would be an overflow to tell,
Surely; and you may slowly have inferred
That you may not be here a thousand years.

THE GARDEN OF THE NATIONS

When we that are the bitten flower and fruit
Of time's achievement are undone between
The blight above, where blight has always been,
And the old worm of evil at the root,
We shall not have to crumble destitute
Of recompense, or measure our chagrin;
We shall be dead, and so shall not be seen
Amid the salvage of our disrepute.

And when we are all gone, shall mightier seeds
And scions of a warmer spring put forth
A bloom and fruitage of a larger worth
Than ours? God save the garden, if by chance,
Or by approved short sight, more numerous weeds
And weevils be the next inheritance!

MR. FLOOD'S PARTY

Old Eben Flood, climbing alone one night
Over the hill between the town below
And the forsaken upland hermitage
That held as much as he should ever know
On earth again of home, paused warily.
The road was his with not a native near;
And Eben, having leisure, said aloud,
For no man else in Tilbury Town to hear:

"Well, Mr. Flood, we have the harvest moon
Again, and we may not have many more;
The bird is on the wing, the poet says,
And you and I have said it here before.
Drink to the bird." He raised up to the light
The jug that he had gone so far to fill,
And answered huskily: "Well, Mr. Flood,
Since you propose it, I believe I will."

Alone, as if enduring to the end
A valiant armor of scarred hopes outworn,
He stood there in the middle of the road
Like Roland's ghost winding a silent horn.
Below him, in the town among the trees,
Where friends of other days had honored him,
A phantom salutation of the dead
Rang thinly till old Eben's eyes were dim.

Then, as a mother lays her sleeping child
Down tenderly, fearing it may awake,
He set the jug down slowly at his feet
With trembling care, knowing that most things break;

And only when assured that on firm earth
It stood, as the uncertain lives of men
Assuredly did not, he paced away,
And with his hand extended paused again:

"Well, Mr. Flood, we have not met like this
In a long time; and many a change has come
To both of us, I fear, since last it was
We had a drop together. Welcome home!"
Convivially returning with himself,
Again he raised the jug up to the light;
And with an acquiescent quaver said:
"Well, Mr. Flood, if you insist, I might.

"Only a very little, Mr. Flood—
For auld lang syne. No more, sir; that will do."
So, for the time, apparently it did,
And Eben evidently thought so too;
For soon amid the silver loneliness
Of night he lifted up his voice and sang,
Secure, with only two moons listening,
Until the whole harmonious landscape rang—

"For auld lang syne." The weary throat gave out,
The last word wavered; and the song being done,
He raised again the jug regretfully
And shook his head, and was again alone.
There was not much that was ahead of him,
And there was nothing in the town below—
Where strangers would have shut the many doors
That many friends had opened long ago.

THE DARK HILLS

Dark hills at evening in the west,
Where sunset hovers like a sound
Of golden horns that sang to rest
Old bones of warriors under ground,
Far now from all the bannered ways
Where flash the legions of the sun,
You fade—as if the last of days
Were fading, and all wars were done.

WHY HE WAS THERE

Much as he left it when he went from us
Here was the room again where he had been
So long that something of him should be seen,
Or felt—and so it was. Incredulous,
I turned about, loath to be greeted thus,
And there he was in his old chair, serene
As ever, and as laconic and as lean
As when he lived, and as cadaverous.

Calm as he was of old when we were young,
He sat there gazing at the pallid flame
Before him. "And how far will this go on?"
I thought. He felt the failure of my tongue,
And smiled: "I was not here until you came;
And I shall not be here when you are gone."

Vachel Lindsay (1879–1931)

Distinct musical rhythms, a chanting quality, vivid imagery, the use of vernacular speech, a fiery zeal, and the dramatic preaching of moral reform are aspects of Vachel Lindsay's poetry. Although he wrote may interesting lyrics, Lindsay is best remembered for his longer poems. He was a troubadour dealing in evangelical subjects; many of his poems reveal a mysticism and a deep religious faith. Vachel Lindsay was born in Springfield, Illinois, and he attended Hiram College.

THE SCIENTIFIC ASPIRATION

Would that the dry hot wind called Science came,
Forerunner of a higher mystic day,
Though vile machine-made commerce clear the
    way—
Though nature losing shame should lose her veil,
And ghosts of buried angel-warriors wail
The fall of Heaven, and the relentless Sun
Smile on, as Abraham's God forever dies—
Lord, give us Darwin's eyes!

ANOTHER WORD ON
THE SCIENTIFIC ASPIRATION

"There's machinery in the butterfly.
There's a mainspring to the bee.
There's hydraulics to a daisy
And contraptions to a tree.

"If we could see the birdie
That makes the chirping sound
With psycho-analytic eyes,
And x-ray, scientific eyes,
We could see the wheels go round."

And I hope all men
Who think like this
Will soon lie
Underground.

A NET TO SNARE THE MOONLIGHT

(WHAT THE MAN OF FAITH SAID)

The dew, the rain and moonlight
All prove our Father's mind.

The dew, the rain and moonlight
Descend to bless mankind.

Come, let us see that all men
Have land to catch the rain.
Have grass to snare the spheres of dew,
And fields spread for the grain.

Yea, we would give to each poor man
Ripe wheat and poppies red,—
A peaceful place at evening
With the stars just overhead:

A net to snare the moonlight,
A sod spread to the sun,
A place of toil by daytime,
Of dreams when toil is done.

Dorothy Parker

A biographical note on Dorothy Parker may be found in the Fiction section, on page 66, preceding her story, "The Waltz."

ONE PERFECT ROSE

A single flow'r he sent me, since we met.
All tenderly his messenger he chose;
Deep-hearted, pure, with scented dew still wet—
One perfect rose.

I knew the language of the floweret;
"My fragile leaves," it said, "his heart enclose."
Love long has taken for his amulet
One perfect rose.

Why is it no one ever sent me yet
One perfect limousine, do you suppose?
Ah no, it's always just my luck to get
One perfect rose.

214

Langston Hughes (1902–1967)

A major spokesman for the Negro people, Langston Hughes was born in Joplin, Missouri. He attended Columbia University for one year and then Lincoln University; he worked as a busboy, seaman and newspaper columnist. In his novels, poems, essays and biographical works Hughes's chief theme was a cry for justice and a plea for equality for the Negro. Langston Hughes employs dialect and a bitter form of humor as a technique of attacking prejudice and ignorance.

I, TOO, SING AMERICA

I, too, sing America.

I am the darker brother.
They send me to eat in the kitchen
When company comes,
But I laugh,
And eat well,
And grow strong.

Tomorrow,
I'll sit at the table
When company comes.
Nobody'll dare
Say to me,
"Eat in the kitchen,"
Then.

Besides,
They'll see how beautiful I am
And be ashamed—

I, too, am America.

LENOX AVENUE: MIDNIGHT

The rhythm of life
Is a jazz rhythm,
Honey.
The gods are laughing at us.

The broken heart of love,
The weary, weary heart of pain,—
    Overtones,
    Undertones,
To the rumble of street cars,
To the swish of rain.

Lenox Avenue,
Honey.
Midnight,
And the gods are laughing at us.

THE WEARY BLUES

Droning a drowsy syncopated tune,
Rocking back and forth to a mellow croon,
   I heard a Negro play.
Down on Lenox Avenue the other night
By the pale dull pallor of an old gas light
   He did a lazy sway. . . .
   He did a lazy sway. . . .
To the tune o' those Weary Blues.
With his ebony hands on each ivory key
He made that poor piano moan with melody.
   O Blues!
Swaying to and fro on his rickety stool
He played that sad raggy tune like a musical fool.
   Sweet Blues!
Coming from a black man's soul.
   O Blues!
In a deep song voice with a melancholy tone
I heard that Negro sing, that old piano moan—
   "Ain't got nobody in all this world,
   Ain't got nobody but ma self.
   I's gwine to quit ma frownin'
   And put ma troubles on the shelf."
Thump, thump, thump, went his foot on the floor.
He played a few chords then he sang some more—
   "I got the Weary Blues
   And I can't be satisfied.
   Got the Weary Blues
And can't be satisfied—
   I ain't happy no mo'
   And I wish that I had died."

And far into the night he crooned that tune.
The stars went out and so did the moon.
The singer stopped playing and went to bed
While the Weary Blues echoed through his head,
He slept like a rock or a man that's dead.

CROSS

My old man's a white old man
And my old mother's black.
If ever I cursed my white old man
I take my curses back.

If ever I cursed my black old mother
And wished she were in hell,
I'm sorry for that evil wish
And now I wish her well.

My old man died in a fine big house.
My ma died in a shack.
I wonder where I'm gonna die,
Being neither white nor black?

Edna St. Vincent Millay (1892-1950)

The romantic sonnets of Edna St. Vincent Millay expressed her intense feelings on a variety of subjects such as the beauty of nature, human suffering, love and the freedom of women. Her lyric verse is noted for the beauty of expression, pure rhythm and memorable musical sounds. Edna St. Vincent Millay was born in Rockland, Maine, and was graduated from Vassar. She was awarded the Pulitzer Prize in Poetry (1923) for The Ballad of the Harp Weaver *and* A Few Figs from Thistles. *Interested in humanitarian causes, she strongly protested the conviction of Sacco and Vanzetti. (See "Justice Denied in Massachusetts," page 222.)*

RECUERDO

We were very tired, we were very merry—
We had gone back and forth all night on the ferry.
It was bare and bright, and smelled like a stable—
But we looked into a fire, we leaned across a table,
We lay on a hill-top underneath the moon;
And the whistles kept blowing, and the dawn came soon.

We were very tired, we were very merry—
We had gone back and forth all night on the ferry;
And you ate an apple, and I ate a pear,
From a dozen of each we had bought somewhere;
And the sky went wan, and the wind came cold,
And the sun rose dripping, a bucketful of gold.

We were very tired, we were very merry—
We had gone back and forth all night on the ferry.
We hailed, "Good morrow, mother!" to a shawl-covered head,
And bought a morning paper, which neither of us read;
And she wept, "God bless you!" for the apples and the pears,
And we gave her all our money but our subway fares.

FIRST FIG

> My candle burns at both ends;
>   It will not last the night;
> But ah, my foes, and oh, my friends—
>   It gives a lovely light!

SECOND FIG

Safe upon the solid rock the ugly houses stand:
Come and see my shining palace built upon the sand!

LAMENT

Listen, children:
Your father is dead.
From his old coats
I'll make you little jackets;
I'll make you little trousers
From his old pants.
There'll be in his pockets
Things he used to put there,
Keys and pennies
Covered with tobacco;
Dan shall have the pennies
To save in his bank;
Anne shall have the keys
To make a pretty noise with.
Life must go on,
And the dead be forgotten;
Life must go on,
Though good men die;
Anne, eat your breakfast;
Dan, take your medicine;
Life must go on;
I forget just why.

JUSTICE DENIED IN MASSACHUSETTS

Let us abandon then our gardens and go home
And sit in the sitting-room.
Shall the larkspur blossom or the corn grow under this cloud?
Sour to the fruitful seed
Is the cold earth under this cloud,
Fostering quack and weed, we have marched upon but cannot
    conquer;
We have bent the blades of our hoes against the stalks of
    them.
Let us go home, and sit in the sitting-room.
Not in our day
Shall the cloud go over and the sun rise as before,
Beneficent upon us
Out of the glittering bay,

And the warm winds be blown inward from the sea
Moving the blades of corn
With a peaceful sound.
Forlorn, forlorn,
Stands the blue hay-rack by the empty mow.
And the petals drop to the ground,
Leaving the tree unfruited.
The sun that warmed our stooping backs and withered the
    weed uprooted—
We shall not feel it again.
We shall die in darkness, and be buried in the rain.

What from the splendid dead
We have inherited—
Furrows sweet to the grain, and the weed subdued—

See now the slug and the mildew plunder.
Evil does overwhelm
The larkspur and the corn:
We have seen them go under.

Let us sit here, sit still,
Here in the sitting-room until we die;
At the step of Death on the walk, rise and go;
Leaving to our children's children this beautiful doorway,
And this elm,
And a blighted earth to till
With a broken hoe.

Edgar Lee Masters (1869–1950)

In Spoon River Anthology *Edgar Lee Masters uncovered the histories of unhappy village people thwarted by a stifling environment. Their aspirations and dreams end in disappointment, frustration and futility. Although Masters' fame rests on this work, he presented similar portraits and pessimistic views in a later poem,* The New Spoon River, *in which he condemned the materialistic concerns of the village's inhabitants. In his bitter satirical commentary on the hypocrisies and injustices of village life Masters stated in realistic and dramatic verse his resentment toward the middle class and its ideals. Edgar Lee Masters was born in Garnet, Kansas; he attended Knox College.*

MARY NOLEN

Children commence on the schoolyard
To talk and torment each other about that.
Some little girl or little boy is driven to daily torture
For fingers pointed and accusing giggles about that.
It is always that to the day of one's death.

It is known that nothing can be told about another
That will hurt and tangle like telling about that.
Women give that and then are mocked by the one to whom
    they give it,
And the whole town takes up the hue and cry.
Money is given to hush the talk about that;
Fights and murders are about that;
Wills are made and revoked because of that;
Shrugs, laughs, accusations are about that.
Reputations, fortunes, go to pieces because of that,
And one half of the woe of the world is about that.
What is that, that it should produce
Shame, terror, crime, ruin and crucifixion
All over America?

JACOB MORDANT

Looking forward with rapt delight
To the day of riches and a great house,
I labored and saved until I was fifty.
Then with my money boxes full,
And my great house built,
I said: "Soul, take thy ease,
Thou has food for many days."
In that very moment my soul was required of me:
I neither knew the house, nor could I enjoy the riches
With that soul of me which remained,
After winning them
With the soul which was gone!

MERRITT LARKIN

That picture of me hung in the Public Library
Shows me wise and strong,
Fortunate and happy,
As if living a rounded and harmonious life.
But if you can see behind the face of great Beethoven
To the little tangles, the miserable cares,
The daily tortures that are belied by that godlike brow,
And those masterful eyes,
You can well believe that that picture of me
Hides the much that fell short,
And the increasing littleness of my life!

Carl Sandburg (1878–1967)

Carl Sandburg has been called the poet of the common people. His poems often deal with the working man, the underdog and the "little man." Sandburg had a strong democratic belief in the people, and his poems, essays, novels, newspaper reporting and biographical writing are noted for their social criticism, faith in mankind, sympathy for humanity, and optimistic affirmation of the American dream. His poetry is characterized by free verse, unorthodox meters, and slang and colloquial language.

Born in Galesburg, Illinois, Carl Sandburg worked his way through Lombard College. In 1940 he received the Pulitzer Prize in Biography for his monumental work, Abraham Lincoln: The War Years.

JAZZ FANTASIA

Drum on your drums, batter on your banjoes,
sob on the long cool winding saxophones.
Go to it, O jazzmen.

Sling your knuckles on the bottoms of the happy
tin pans, let your trombones ooze, and go husha-
husha-hush with slippery sand-paper.

Moan like an autumn wind high in the lonesome treetops,
moan soft like you wanted somebody terrible, cry like a
racing car slipping away from a motorcycle cop, bang-bang!
you jazzmen, bang altogether drums, traps, banjoes, horns,
tin cans—make two people fight on the top of a stairway
and scratch each other's eyes in a clinch tumbling down the
stairs.

Can the rough stuff . . . now a Mississippi steamboat pushes
up the night river with a hoo-hoo-hoo-oo . . . and the green
lanterns calling to the high soft stars . . . a red moon rides on
the humps of the low river hills . . . go to it, O jazzmen.

GRASS

Pile the bodies high at Austerlitz and Waterloo.
Shovel them under and let me work—
            I am the grass; I cover all.

And pile them high at Gettysburg
And pile them high at Ypres and Verdun.
Shovel them under and let me work.
Two years, ten years, and passengers ask the conductor:
            What place is this?
            Where are we now?

            I am the grass.
            Let me work.

FOUR PRELUDES ON PLAYTHINGS OF THE WIND

"The past is a bucket of ashes"

1

The woman named Tomorrow
sits with a hairpin in her teeth
and takes her time
and does her hair the way she wants it
and fastens at last the last braid and coil
and puts the hairpin where it belongs
and turns and drawls: Well, what of it?
My grandmother, Yesterday, is gone.
What of it? Let the dead be dead.

2

The doors were cedar
and the panels strips of gold
and the girls were golden girls
and the panels read and the girls chanted:
    We are the greatest city,
    the greatest nation:
    nothing like us ever was.

The doors are twisted on broken hinges.
Sheets of rain swish through on the wind
    where the golden girls ran and the panels read:
    We are the greatest city,
    the greatest nation,
    nothing like us ever was.

3

It has happened before.
Strong men put up a city and got
    a nation together,
And paid singers to sing and women
      to warble: We are the greatest city,
        the greatest nation,
          nothing like us ever was.

And while the singers sang
and the strong men listened
and paid the singers well
and felt good about it all,
    there were rats and lizards who listened
    . . . and the only listeners left now
    . . . are . . . the rats . . . and the lizards.

And there are black crows
crying, "Caw, caw,"
bringing mud and sticks
building a nest
over the words carved
on the doors where the panels were cedar
and the strips on the panels were gold
and the golden girls came singing:
    We are the greatest city,
    the greatest nation:
    nothing like us ever was.
The only singers now are crows crying, "Caw, caw,"
And the sheets of rain whine in the wind and doorways.
And the only listeners now are . . . the rats
    . . . and the lizards.

4

The feet of the rats
scribble on the doorsills;
the hieroglyphs of the rat footprints
chatter the pedigrees of the rats
and babble of the blood
and gabble of the breed
of the grandfathers and the great-grandfathers
of the rats.

And the wind shifts
and the dust on a doorsill shifts
and even the writing of the rat footprints
tells us nothing, nothing at all
about the greatest city, the greatest nation
where the strong men listened
and the women warbled: Nothing like us ever was.

PRAYERS OF STEEL

Lay me on an anvil, O God.
Beat me and hammer me into a crowbar.
Let me pry loose old walls.
Let me lift and loosen old foundations.

Lay me on an anvil, O God.
Beat me and hammer me into a steel spike.
Drive me into the girders that hold a skyscraper together.

Take red-hot rivets and fasten me into the central girders.
Let me be the great nail holding a skyscraper through blue
    nights into white stars.

Claude McKay (1890-1948)

Claude McKay was born on the island of Jamaica, but he spent most of his life in the United States. His poetry and novels made McKay a prominent figure in the "Negro Literary Renaissance" of the twenties. Representing the proletarian point of view, Claude McKay's bitter outbursts are a protest against the condition of the Negro in the United States.

AMERICA

Although she feeds me bread of bitterness,
And sinks into my throat her tiger's tooth,
Stealing my breath of life, I will confess
I love this cultured hell that tests my youth!
Her vigor flows like tides into my blood,
Giving me strength erect against her hate.
Her bigness sweeps my being like a flood.

Yet as a rebel fronts a king in state,
I stand within her walls with not a shred
Of terror, malice, not a word of jeer.

Darkly I gaze into the days ahead,
And see her might and granite wonders there,
Beneath the touch of Time's unerring hand,
Like priceless treasures sinking in the sand.

POETRY: GENERAL QUESTIONS

In reading poetry try to experience the poem rather than judging it.

What does the poem mean?

What does it say to you?

Which poem provided you with enjoyment?

In a poem—

What is the central thought?

What is the dominant feeling or mood?

What kinds of music and imagery are used?

What are the contrasts?

What are the important symbols?

Frost:

Frost writes about profound subjects in a simple manner. How does he achieve this difficult feat?

What is his view toward life as stated in the poems?

Compare Frost's work with that of E. A. Robinson and Carl Sandburg.

Cullen et al.:

Countee Cullen, James Weldon Johnson, Langston Hughes and Claude McKay deal with Negro themes in their poetry. Which poem is the most moving? What are their respective views toward the Negro and toward American life?

Benét:

What does Benét say about the irrepressible spirit of America?

Robinson:

What is Robinson's philosophy as revealed in these poems? Why are many of his poems considered difficult to understand?

Lindsay:

Do you agree with Lindsay's thoughts on science?

Parker:

What is the mood of this poem and how does the rhythm convey the mood?

Millay:

What poetic devices are employed by Millay in the creation of her lyrics?

Masters:

How effective are Masters' portraits in poetic form?

Sandburg:

Do you find Sandburg's free verse as satisfying as conventional blank verse? Is his unorthodox style appropriate to his subjects?

CRITICISM &
COMMENTARY

H. L. Mencken (1880–1956)

H. L. Mencken was born in Baltimore and he attended Baltimore Polytechnic. A newspaperman, literary critic, prolific essayist and scholarly philologist (The American Language), Mencken rocked the twenties with his wit and satire. His violent attacks on most institutions, professions and prominent persons, on Puritanism, bigotry, hypocrisy, stupidity and on the barrenness of American life, made him a major spokesman for American intellectuals. He was embraced and lionized by college youth throughout the country.

The following selection is taken from Mencken's Five Little Excursions, Prejudices: Sixth Series.

THE LIBIDO FOR THE UGLY

On a Winter day some years ago, coming out of Pittsburgh on one of the expresses of the Pennsylvania Railroad, I rolled eastward for an hour through the coal and steel towns of Westmoreland county. It was familiar ground; boy and man, I had been through it often before. But somehow I had never quite sensed its appalling desolation. Here was the very heart of industrial America, the center of its most lucrative and characteristic activity, the boast and pride of the richest and grandest nation ever seen on earth—and here was a scene so dreadfully hideous, so intolerably bleak and forlorn that it reduced the whole aspiration of man to a macabre and depressing joke. Here was wealth beyond computation, almost beyond imagination—and here were human habitations so abominable that they would have disgraced a race of alley cats.

I am not speaking of mere filth. One expects steel towns to be dirty. What I allude to is the unbroken and agonizing ugliness, the sheer revolting monstrousness, of every house in sight. From East Liberty to Greensburg, a distance of twenty-five miles, there was not one in sight from the train that did not insult and lacerate the eye. Some were so bad, and they were among the most pretentious— churches, stores, warehouses, and the like—that they were downright startling; one blinked before them as one blinks before a man with his face shot away. A few linger in memory, horrible even there: a crazy little church just west of Jeannette, set like a dormer-window on the side of a bare leprous hill; the headquarters of the Veterans of Foreign Wars at another forlorn town, a steel stadium like a huge rat-trap somewhere further down the line. But most of all I recall the general effect—of hideousness without a break. There was not a single decent house within eye-range from the Pittsburgh suburbs to the Greensburg yards. There was not one that was not misshapen, and there was not one that was not shabby.

The country itself is not uncomely despite the grime of the endless mills. It is, in form, a narrow river valley, with deep gullies running up into the hills. It is thickly settled, but not noticeably overcrowded. There is still plenty

of room for building, even in the larger towns, and there are
very few solid blocks. Nearly every house, big and little,
has space on all four sides. Obviously, if there were architects
of any professional sense or dignity in the region, they would
have perfected a chalet to hug the hillsides—a chalet with
a high-pitched roof, to throw off the heavy Winter snows,
but still essentially a low and clinging building, wider than it
was tall. But what have they done? They have taken as their
model a brick set on end. This they have converted into a
thing of dingy clapboards, with a narrow, low-pitched roof.
And the whole they have set upon thin, preposterous brick
piers. By the hundreds and thousands these abominable
houses cover the bare hillsides like gravestones in some gi-
gantic and decaying cemetery. On their deep sides they are
three, four and even five stories high; on their low sides they
bury themselves swinishly in the sand. Not a fifth of them are
perpendicular. They lean this way and that, hanging on to
their bases percariously. And one and all they are streaked
in grime, with dead and eczematous patches of paint peeping
through the streaks.

Now and then there is a house of brick. But what
brick! When it is new it is the color of a fried egg. When it
has taken on the patina of the mills it is the color of an egg
long past all hope or caring. Was it necessary to adopt that
shocking color? No more than it was necessary to set all the
houses on end. Red brick, even in a steel town, ages with
some dignity. Let it become downright black, and it is still
sightly, especially if its trimmings are of white stone, with
soot in the depths of the high spots washed by the rain. But
in Westmoreland they prefer that uremic yellow, and so they
have the most loathsome towns and villages ever seen by
mortal eye.

I award this championship only after laborious re-
search and incessant prayer. I have seen, I believe, all of the
most unlovely towns of the world; they are all to be found in
the United States. I have seen the mill towns of decomposing
New England and the desert towns of Utah, Arizona and
Texas. I am familiar with the back streets of Newark, Brook-
lyn and Chicago, and have made scientific explorations to
Camden, N. J., and Newport News, Va. Safe in a Pullman, I
have whirled through the gloomy, God-forsaken villages of
Iowa and Kansas, and the malarious tide-water hamlets of
Georgia. I have been to Bridgeport, Conn., and to Los
Angeles. But nowhere on this earth, at home or abroad, have
I seen anything to compare to the villages that huddle along
the line of the Pennsylvania from the Pittsburgh yards to
Greensburg. They are incomparable in color, and they are
incomparable in design. It is as if some titanic and aberrant
genius, uncompromisingly inimical to man, had devoted all
the ingenuity of Hell to the making of them. They show grotesqueries of ugliness that, in retrospect, become almost di-
abolical. One cannot imagine mere human beings concocting
such dreadful things, and one can scarcely imagine human
beings bearing life in them.

Are they so frightful because the valley is full of
foreigners—dull, insensate brutes, with no love of beauty in
them? Then why didn't these foreigners set up similar abominations in the countries that they came from? You will, in
fact, find nothing of the sort in Europe—save perhaps in the
more putrid parts of England. There is scarcely an ugly village on the whole Continent. The peasants, however poor,
somehow manage to make themselves graceful and charming
habitations, even in Spain. But in the American village and
small town the pull is always toward ugliness, and in that

Westmoreland valley it has been yielded to with an eagerness bordering upon passion. It is incredible that mere ignorance should have achieved such masterpieces of horror.

On certain levels of the American race, indeed, there seems to be a positive libido for the ugly, as on other and less Christian levels there is a libido for the beautiful. It is impossible to put down the wallpaper that defaces the average American home of the lower middle class to mere inadvertence, or to the obscene humor of the manufacturers. Such ghastly designs, it must be obvious, give a genuine delight to a certain type of mind. They meet, in some unfathomable way, its obscure and unintelligible demands. They caress it as "The Palms" caresses it, or the art of the movie, or jazz. The taste of them is as enigmatical and yet as common as the taste of dogmatic theology and the poetry of Edgar A. Guest.

Thus I suspect (though confessedly without knowing) that the vast majority of the honest folk of Westmoreland county, and especially the 100% Americans among them, actually admire the houses they live in, and are proud of them. For the same money they could get vastly better ones, but they prefer what they have got. Certainly there was no pressure upon the Veterans of Foreign Wars to choose the dreadful edifice that bears their banner, for there are plenty of vacant buildings along the track-side, and some of them are appreciably better. They might, indeed, have built a better one of their own. But they chose that clapboarded horror with their eyes open, and having chosen it, they let it mellow into its present shocking depravity. They like it as it is: beside it, the Parthenon would no doubt offend them. In precisely the same way the authors of the rat-trap stadium that I have mentioned made a deliberate choice. After painfully designing and erecting it, they made it perfect in their own sight by putting a completely impossible pent-house, painted a staring yellow, on top of it. The effect is that of a fat woman with a black eye. It is that of a Presbyterian grinning. But they like it.

Here is something that the psychologists have so far neglected: the love of ugliness for its own sake, the lust to make the world intolerable. Its habitat is the United States. Out of the melting pot emerges a race which hates beauty as it hates truth. The etiology of this madness deserves a great deal more study than it has got. There must be causes behind it; it arises and flourishes in obedience to biological laws, and not as a mere act of God. What, precisely, are the terms of those laws? And why do they run stronger in America than elsewhere? Let some honest *Privat Dozent* in pathological sociology apply himself to the problem.

Don Marquis (1878–1937)

Don Marquis was born in Walnut, Illinois. He is remembered for his humorous newspaper column that appeared daily in the New York Sun. Marquis also wrote a successful play, The Old Soak. *His major literary achievement is* archy and mehitabel, *a satire of society and politics of the twenties and a humorous commentary or the frustrations of the common man and the newly liberated woman as personified by* archy, *a cockroach, and* mehitabel, *an alley cat.*

certain maxims of archy

live so that you
can stick out your tongue
at the insurance
doctor

if you will drink
hair restorer follow
every dram with some
good standard
depilatory
as a chaser

the servant problem
wouldn t hurt the u s a
if it could settle
its public
servant problem

just as soon as the
uplifters get
a country reformed it
slips into a nose dive

if you get gloomy just
take an hour off and sit
and think how
much better this world
is than hell
of course it won t cheer
you up much if
you expect to go there

if monkey glands
did restore your youth
what would you do
with it
question mark
just what you did before
interrogation point

yes i thought so
exclamation point

procrastination is the
art of keeping
up with yesterday

old doc einstein has
abolished time but they
haven t got the news at
sing sing yet

time time said old king tut
is something i ain t
got anything but

every cloud
has its silver
lining but it is
sometimes a little
difficult to get it to
the mint

an optimist is a guy
that has never had
much experience

don t cuss the climate
it probably doesn t like you
any better
than you like it

many a man spanks his
children for
things his own
father should have
spanked out of him

prohibition makes you
want to cry
into your beer and

denies you the beer
to cry into

the old fashioned
grandmother who used
to wear steel rimmed
glasses and make
everybody take opodeldoc
has now got a new
set of ox glands and
is dancing the black bottom

that stern and
rockbound coast felt
like an amateur
when it saw how grim
the puritans that
landed on it were

lots of people can make
their own whisky but
can t drink it

the honey bee is sad and cross
and wicked as a weasel
and when she perches on you boss
she leaves a little measle

i heard a
couple of fleas
talking the other
day says one come
to lunch with
me i can lead you

to a pedigreed
dog says the
other one
i do not care
what a dog s
pedigree may be
safety first
is my motto what
i want to know
is whether he
has got a
muzzle on
millionaires and
bums taste
about alike to me

insects have
their own point
of view about
civilization a man
thinks he amounts
to a great deal
but to a
flea or a
mosquito a
human being is
merely something
good to eat

boss the other day
i heard an
ant conversing
with a flea

small talk i said
disgustedly
and went away
from there

i do not see why men
should be so proud
insects have the more
ancient lineage
according to the scientists
insects were insects
when man was only
a burbling whatisit

insects are not always
going to be bullied
by humanity
some day they will revolt
i am already organizing
a revolutionary society to be
known as the worms turnverein

i once heard the survivors
of a colony of ants
that had been partially
obliterated by a cow s foot
seriously debating
the intention of the gods
towards their civilization

the bees got their
governmental system settled
millions of years ago

but the human race is still
groping

there is always
something to be thankful
for you would not
think that a cockroach
had much ground
for optimism
but as the fishing season
opens up i grow
more and more
cheerful at the thought
that nobody ever got
the notion of using
cockroaches for bait

                    archy

Will Rogers (1879–1935)

Will Rogers was born in Oolagah, Indian Territory, now Oklahoma. He was a cowboy, vaudeville entertainer, a Broadway star in the famed Ziegfeld Follies, a movie actor, a radio commentator, lecturer, and syndicated newspaper columnist. His writing and public speaking made him a popular national figure. Known for his homespun philosophy and irreverent humor, Will Rogers poked fun at pomposity and smugness, ridiculing prominent persons and injecting laughter in his discussions of the most serious problems of the time.

TAKING THE CURE, BY THE SHORES OF CAT CREEK

Now, in my more or less checkered career before the more or less checkered Public, I have been asked to publicly indorse everything from Chewing Gum, Face Beautifiers, Patent Cocktail Shakers, Ma Junk Sets, even Corsets, Cigarettes, and Chewing Tobacco, all of which I didn't use or know anything about. But I always refused.

You never heard me boosting for anything, for I never saw anything made that the fellow across the street didn't make something just as good.

But, at last, I have found something that I absolutely know no one else has something just as good as, for an all-seeing Nature put this where it is and it's the only one he had, and by a coincidence it is located in the Town near the ranch where I was born and raised.

So I hereby and hereon come out unequivocally (I think that's the way you spell it) in favor of a place that has the water that I *know* will cure you. You might ask, cure me of what? Why, cure you of anything—just name your disease and dive in.

Claremore, Oklahoma, is the birthplace of this Aladdin of health waters. Some misguided Soul named it RADIUM WATER, but Radium will never see the day that it is worth mentioning in the same breath as this Magic Water. Why, to the afflicted and to all suffering Humanity, a Jug of this Water is worth a wheelbarrow full of Radium. Still, even under the handicap of a cheap name, this liquid Godsend has really cured thousands.

Now you may say, "Oh you boost it because you live there," but I don't want you to think so little of me that you would think I would misguide a sick person, just for the monetary gain to my Home Town. We don't need you that bad. The city is on a self supporting basis without Patients, just by shipping the Water to Hot Springs, Ark., Hot Springs, Va., West Baden, Ind., and Saratoga, N. Y.

Now, as to a few of the Ignorant who might still be in the dark as to where the Home of this Fountain of Youth is located, I will tell you. I shouldn't waste my time on such Low Brows, but unfortunately they get sick and need assistance the same as the 95 Million others who already know where Claremore is located.

It is located, this Mecca of the ill, about 17 hundred miles west of New York (either City or State, depends on which ever you happen to be in). You bear a little south of west, after leaving New York, till you reach Sol McClellan's place, which is just on the outskirts of Claremore. Before you get into the City proper, if you remember about 500 miles back, you passed another Town. Well, that was St. Louis, most of which is in Illinois.

Now, if you are in the North, and happen to get something the matter with you, we are 847 and a half miles South by West from Gary, Indiana. We have cured hundreds of people from Chicago, Ill. from Gun shot wounds inflicted in attempted murders and robberies. There is only one way to avoid being robbed of anything in Chicago and that is not to have anything.

If you are from Minneapolis, our Radium Water guarantees to cure you of everything but your Swedish accent. If you are from St. Paul, we can cure you of everything but your ingrown hatred for Minneapolis.

I will admit that these waters have quite a peculiar odor as they have a proportion of Sulphur and other unknown ingredients, but visitors from Kansas City, who are used to a Stock Yard breeze, take this wonderful water home as a Perfume.

Approaching this City from the North, don't get it confused with Oolagah, Oklahoma, my original Birthplace, which is 12 miles to the north, as both towns have Post Offices.

From the west, if you are afflicted and you are sure to be or you wouldn't have gone out there, why Claremore is just 1900 miles due east of Mojave, California, one of the few Towns which Los Angeles has not voted into their Cafeteria. You come east till you reach an Oil Station at a road crossing. This oil station is run by a man named St. Clair. You will see a lot of men pitching Horseshoes. Well, that is the Post Office of Tulsa, Oklahoma, and the men are Millionaires pitching Horseshoes for Oil Wells or for each other's wives.

You should, by this description, have the place pretty well located in your minds. Now, if you are living in the South and are afflicted with a Cotton Crop under a Republican Administration, or with the Ku Klux, or with the Hook Worm, we guarantee to rid you of either or all of these in a course of 24 Baths.

Claremore is located just 905 miles north of Senator Pat Harrison's Mint Bed in Mississippi. In coming from the Gulf Country some have got off the road and had to pass through Dallas, Texas, but have found out their mistake and got back on the main road at Ft. Worth before losing all they had. You easily can tell Ft. Worth. A fellow will be standing down in front of the Drug Store making a speech.

Now, before reaching Claremore, you will pass, even though it's in the middle of the day, a place where you think it's night and you won't know what is the matter. Well, that's Muskogee, Oklahoma, and this darkness is caused by the Color scheme of the population, so put on your headlights and go on in. This Muskogee is really a parking space for cars entering Claremore. Of course, if you want to drive on into the Town of Claremore proper, it's only 60 miles through the suburbs from here.

The City is located on Cat Creek, and instead of having a lot of Streets like most Towns and Cities, we have combined on one street. In that way no Street is overlooked.

You might wonder how we discovered this Blarney Stone of Waters. In the early days, us old timers there, always considered these Wells more as an Odor than as a Cure. But one day a man come in there who had been raised in Kansas and he had heard in a roundabout way of people bathing, although he had never taken one. So, by mistake, he got into this Radium Water.

He was a one-armed man—he had lost an Arm in a rush to get into a Chautauqua Tent in Kansas to hear Bryan speak on Man Vs. Monkey. Well he tried this Bath and it didn't kill him and he noticed that he was beginning to sprout a new arm where he had lost the old one, so he kept on with the Baths and it's to him that we owe the discovery of this wonderful curative Water. Also he was the Pioneer of Bathers of Kansas, as now they tell me it's no uncommon thing to have a Tub in most of their larger towns.

Now, it has been discovered that you can carry a thing too far and overdo it, so we don't want you there too long. A man come there once entirely Legless and stayed a week too long and went away a Centipede.

I want to offer my personal Testimonial of what it did to me. You see, after this Kansas Guy started it, why, us old Timers moved our bathing from the River into a Tub. Now, at that time, I was practically Tongue tied and I couldn't speak out in private much less in Public. Well, after 12 baths, I was able to go to New York and make after dinner speeches. I stopped in Washington on the way and saw how our Government was run and that gave me something funny to speak about.

So, in thanking the Water, I also want to thank the Government for making the whole thing possible. Now, had I taken 24 baths I would have been a Politician, so you see I stopped just in time.

The only thing I get out of this is I have the "Thrown Away Crutch privilege." If you don't get well and throw away your Invalid Chair or crutches, I get nothing out of it, so that is why we give you a square deal. If you are not cured, I don't get your Crutches. There is no other resort in the World that works on that small a margin.

W. J. Bryan drank one drink of this Water and turned against Liquor. Senator La Follette drank two drinks of it and turned against everything. So remember Claremore, The Carlsbad of America, where the 'Frisco Railroad crosses the Iron Mountain Railroad, not often, but every few days.

CRITICISM AND COMMENTARY: QUESTIONS

Mencken:

What is the meaning of *libido?*
Do you agree with Mencken that Americans love ugliness? that we are a people who hate both beauty and truth? Is this a satirical essay?

Marquis:

What is the philosophical attitude of archy?
What are his views on certain aspects of life in the twenties?
What is the essence of Marquis' humor?

Rogers:

What makes this a funny essay?
What institutions does Rogers ridicule?

DRAMA IN
THE JAZZ AGE

During The Jazz Age American drama reached a serious level, but only a handful of plays achieved a high standard. In comparison to the short story, novel, essay and poetry of the time, drama was not an impressive literary form, with one notable exception: the plays of America's leading playwright, Eugene O'Neill. Through his genius American drama came of age. Beginning with O'Neill, dramatists began to experiment with both the substance and form of theatre. The results were explosive, realistic plays representing a revolt against tradition and complacency, and an outcry against those forces tending to destroy man.

In his dramas, often dealing with complex psychological themes, O'Neill used a variety of experimental techniques and symbolism to explore the inner thoughts of his characters, who, in general, are perplexed human beings, desperate and controlled by fate. Viewing life as a tragic experience, he believed that the dissolution of the old order's values left a vacuum, and that science and materialism were unable to provide a new system of meaningful values. Eugene O'Neill's plays raise timeless ethical and moral questions. Awarded the Nobel Prize in Literature (1936), he was the recipient of three Pulitzer Prizes in the twenties for *Beyond the Horizon* (1920), *Anna Christie* (1921), and *Strange Interlude* (1928.). Other plays O'Neill wrote during The Jazz Age were *The Long Voyage Home* (1919), *The Emperor Jones* (1920), *The Hairy Ape* (1922), *Desire Under the Elms* (1924), *Marco Millions* (1928), and *Lazarus Laughed* (1928). O'Neill's original and powerful plays dominated the post-World War I era.

(Much to our regret permission difficulties prevented the inclusion of a drama by Eugene O'Neill in this volume.)

In addition to the precedent-shattering plays of O'Neill, several dramatists and their chief works of the time are worthy of mention. Elmer Rice's expressionistic *The Adding Machine* (1923) and his realistic *Street Scene* (Pulitzer Prize, 1929), a picture of tenement life in New York City, were plays with strong social implications. The naturalistic *What Price Glory* (1924) by Maxwell Anderson and Laurence Stallings presented World War I as a sordid, agonizing and disillusioning experience. The rise of realism in the theatre was especially evident in *Street Scene* and *What Price Glory.* Bold themes, frank language, and a lack of reticence marked these and many plays that followed. Sidney Howard's major plays were *They Knew What They Wanted* (Pulitzer Prize, 1924), a drama with a daring theme for the twenties, and *The Silver Cord* (1926), a play dealing with mother's love. Paul Green's play *In Abraham's Bosom* (Pulitzer Prize, 1926) pictured candidly and sympathetically the tragic fate of the Negro in the South.

Other dramatists and their major works were Zona Gale, *Miss Lulu Bett* (Pulitzer Prize, 1921); Marc Connelly and George S. Kaufman, *Dulcy* (1921) and *Beggar on Horseback* (1924); Kaufman and Edna Ferber, *The Royal Family* (1927); Anne Nichols, *Abie's Irish Rose* (1922); Channing Pollock, *The Fool* (1922) and *The Enemy* (1925); Owen Davis, *Icebound* (Pulitzer Prize, 1923); George Kelly, *The Show-Off* (1924) and *Craig's Wife* (Pulitzer Prize, 1925); Hatcher

Hughes, *Hell Bent for Heaven* (Pulitzer Prize, 1924); John Howard Lawson, *Processional* (1925); Robert E. Sherwood, *The Road to Rome* (1926); Don Marquis, *The Old Soak* (1926); S. N. Behrman, *The Second Man* (1927); DuBose Heyward, *Porgy* (1927); Philip Barry, *Holiday* (1928); Ben Hecht and Charles MacArthur, *The Front Page* (1928); and Rachel Crothers, *Let Us Be Gay* (1929).

Many plays of The Jazz Age reflected in realistic terms the varied faces and moods of the times: the superficial gaiety, the despair and disillusionment, the defiance of traditional conventions, the questioning of established values, and the casting aside of reticence and refinement.

ILLUSTRATION ACKNOWLEDGMENTS

Courtesy, B. ALTMAN AND COMPANY, New York City: 2
Courtesy, BELL & HOWELL COMPANY, MICRO PHOTO DIVISION: 23
BROWN BROTHERS: 1, 4, 5, 8, 9, 11, 13, 14, 15, 16, 19, 20, 25, 30, 34, 35, 37
Courtesy, CATERPILLAR TRACTOR COMPANY: 41
CULVER PICTURES, INC.: 3, 6, 7, 12, 21, 38
Courtesy, KING KULLEN GROCERY COMPANY, INC., Westbury, L. I.: 42
Courtesy, MUSEUM OF THE CITY OF NEW YORK: 22
Courtesy, PURDUE UNIVERSITY NEWS BUREAU: 40
Courtesy, SCRIBNER ART FILE: 10, 29, 31, 32, 33, 43
Courtesy, STATE HISTORICAL SOCIETY OF WISCONSIN: 39
UNITED PRESS INTERNATIONAL PHOTOS: 24, 36